OUT OF THIS WORLD
american space photography

PAUL DICKSON **OUT OF**
"american

THIS WORLD
space photography

With a Foreword by R. Buckminster Fuller

A DELTA SPECIAL

Visual Studies Workshop
Research Center
Rochester, N.Y.

1-27-78

A DELTA SPECIAL
Published by
Dell Publishing Co., Inc.
1 Dag Hammarskjold Plaza
New York, New York 10017

Photographs courtesy of the National Aeronautics and Space Administration and the National Environmental Satellite Service

Delta ® TM 755118, Dell Publishing Co., Inc.

ISBN: 0-440-56756-4

Printed in the United States of America

First Delta printing—October 1977

Designed by Elaine Golt Gongora

Contents

Acknowledgments

A number of kind and knowledgeable individuals have been of help in locating images and information for this book. Special thanks are due Mary F. Wyvill of the National Environmental Satellite Service, Dr. Paul D. Lohman of the Goddard Spaceflight Center, Donald L. Zylstra of NASA's Office of Public Affairs, and the staff of the Audio-Visual News Branch at NASA headquarters, which is headed by Les Gaver.

Foreword

In 1786, Robert Burns, the Scottish poet, said, "Oh wad some power the giftie gie us/To see oursels as others see us!" God gave us that gift when the first electromagnetically transmitted photograph of the planet Earth, as seen from the Moon, was received by humans back here on Earth. This occurred in the three millionth year of human presence aboard Spaceship Earth (as scientifically established by the Leakeys). We date that Moon view of ourselves as "August twenty-third, nineteen hundred and sixty-six," which manifests how generally shortsighted is our "Western world's" "practical, everyday" view of our Earthian affairs.

Though God gave us the gift to see ourselves as others elsewhere than on Earth might see us, we humans aboard our planet Earth continue to see ourselves only as our misinformedly conditioned brain-imagining "sees us." As the astronauts returned from their first trip to the Moon, the president of the United States congratulated them for "getting safely *up* to the Moon and back *down* to Earth again." As the president had not been through the astronauts' training and experience, this seemed a reasonable instance of misconditioned reflexes. The astronauts themselves, however, as heard over the television from the Moon, spoke about "being up here on the Moon." At the moment I heard them say this, they and the Moon, zooming together with the Earth around the Sun at 60,000 miles per hour, were on the other side of the Earth in the direction of my feet.

The correct words, of course, are "in, out, and around": into the Moon, into Mars, into Earth. "In" is always one-directionally unique and is "in"dividually point-to-able. "Out" is any direction. You go in to go out because *out* is not only any direction, it is all directions. Electromagnetically speaking, it is tuned "out." "In" is what we are thinking about now. "In" is the momentary reality into which we are "tuned." All the rest is, for the moment, tuned out but equally real as it is progressively tuned "in." Physics finds that the universe has no solid *things* surrounded by and interspersed with space. Life is an inventory of in and out tunings. Birth is the first tuning-in; death may not be the last.

As I write the introduction to this truly fascinating book, I find our planet's name spelled with a small "e," even though its 7,926-mile diameter is larger than the diameters of Venus (7620 miles), Mars (4220 miles), Pluto (3600 miles), and Mercury (3010 miles). We honor the first letter of all the other planets' names with a capital letter. I am confident that all the humans born after man

landed on the Moon will spontaneously spell Earth with a capital
"E." The magnificent pictures in this book will help.

Lest the reader feel that I am being unreasonable about humanity's conditioned reflexes, I recall that, on several occasions, I have been asked to speak before sizeable audiences of distinguished scientists, and on these occasions, I have always asked these truthful men "if there are any scientists present who do not 'see' *the Sun going down* each evening when we, the observers, and our Earth's visibly horizoned landscape are rotating eastward around our polar axis to obscure our great celestial 'gas station' from view." I find that all humans are as yet using the words "up" and "down" as a consequence of our millions of years of being overwhelmed by a world vastly greater than ourselves. Our minuteness relative to this has persuaded us to interpret our experience as existence on a "wide, wide," "four-cornered," flat world around which all the bright little celestial "things" revolve.

Those who are about to read this book and to study its pictures are urged to continually ponder our human significance in the universe and to realize that these pictures give us a chance to break loose from our millions of years of self-misinformed fixations. What this book gives us is more than that which Burns asked of God—it gives us a chance to think about the totality of our experience. It gives us a chance to discover to a meager degree that we are indeed integrally functioning components of the great cosmic scheme. This book may enable us to see ourselves as essential episodes in the cosmic scenario of the Eternally Regenerative Universe—which is entropically and visibly exporting here, while syntropically and invisibly importing there, in a nonsimultaneous and dissimilarly enduring complex of overlapping transformative episodes. Eternally Regenerative Universe is the eternal intellectual integrity's only 100% efficient system, which is to say that only cosmic totality is adequate unto itself.

Because light has a unique limit speed of approximately 700 million miles an hour (186,000 miles a second multiplied by sixty times sixty), which speed may also be stated as six and one half trillion miles a year, and because most of our celestial phenomena are so remote to us, when we "see" our polestar (North Star), we are seeing a live show that is occurring 680 years ago and four and one half quadrillion miles away. Looking out into the universe, we see both "away" and "ago." We see four-dimensionally. When we look at the bright star in the end of the handle of the "Big Dipper," we are seeing a live show taking place 180 years ago. One of the two bright stars in "Orion's Belt" is a live show taking place 1,500 years ago, the other, 1,000 years ago. When we look at Andromeda, we are seeing a live show taking place one million years ago.

As Einstein said, the universe is an aggregate of nonsimultaneous and only partially overlapping and variously enduring energy transformation episodes, and that is the description of a scenario in which one picture tells us virtually nothing regarding the scenario.

A single frame picture of a caterpillar does not tell us that the caterpillar is going to transform into a butterfly, nor does one picture of a butterfly tell us that it can fly. It requires many sequential frame pictures of the butterfly flying to tell us it can fly, and even a million frames may not tell us how the butterfly accomplishes its flight. Indeed, it might take billions of frames to clarify what role butterflies play in the complex ecology of organic life existing upon our planet Earth, almost all of whose vast energy importing is supplied by our cosmic energy "gas station," the Sun, ninety-two million miles away and eight minutes ago. Billions upon billions of frames of pictures of historically integrative human experience may now begin to suggest how it happens that there are cosmic transformative complexes so comprehensively intricate as to constitute intercomplementary organisms such as human beings and mosquitoes, all of which are directly or indirectly maintained photosynthetically upon the planet Earth by terrestrial ecology and its remote Sun energy source.

Why are humans being given cosmic passage aboard Spaceship Earth? Why are we humans exclusively endowed with minds by means of which we discover and use some of the eternally coexistent, omni-interaccommodative generalized operating principles of cosmic regeneration?

Look closely and comprehensively at these pictures. Integrate your reactions with all your spontaneous recalls of the other experiential information of your life as well as of other lives as reported to you. Think and think some more. From time to time, humans are endowed with the capability to discover just a little more regarding the significance of their role in the cosmic scenario. You too might catch one of these "cosmic fish."

—R. Buckminster Fuller

OUT OF THIS WORLD
american space photography

Quick Focus

At the very beginning, hardly anyone thought of space photography as anything more than a branch of industrial photography. There would, of course, be professional 8 by 10-inch glossy prints of launches, of factories where booster rockets were being assembled, and of astronauts being trained which would be nice to have for their public relations and historic value. But these were pictures *taken on the ground,* and they differed little from those the Air Force would take of a new plane or IBM of a new computer.

Astronauts flying the first missions into space did not even take cameras with them, and when one was finally packed for John Glenn's famous earth orbit in 1962, it was virtually an afterthought. On those early flights just after the Glenn mission when almost everything an astronaut did in space was proclaimed to be "an experiment," taking pictures was deemed to be little more than a recreational extra. Little was expected from those early photos, and policymakers at the fledgling National Aeronautics and Space Administration felt that they would have minimal value, and fretted that taking them might create international ill will, as sovereignty-sensitive nations would resent having their pictures snapped by orbiting Americans.

On another front, there was considerable skepticism about the usefulness of unmanned satellites and space probes as photographic vehicles. In 1958, when, in reaction to the Soviet Sputnik success of October, 1957, Congress was holding hearings leading to the creation of a US space program, several witnesses predicted that robot spacecraft would take daily pictures of the world's weather and send back close-up images of distant planets. As a Congressman with a long and strong interest in the space program recalled recently, "These statements produced a reaction that frankly bordered on the incredulous with no little amusement in many quarters."

As it turned out, space photography quickly became more and more important and soon reached the point at which it was a major element of the space program, for both manned and unmanned missions. The millions of images that have been taken in space since 1960 are the visual glue that holds it all together. They record what has happened and, in the case of the images that are sent back to earth electronically, tell us what is happening. These images make it possible for all of us who have never been in orbit or set foot on the moon to share the excitement of space exploration.

What is more, they have been of remarkable and unprecedented utility. Before we could explore the moon, thousands of photos had to be taken by unmanned probes and lunar orbiters to map the place and to pick the best landing sites. Dozens of satellites have been put into earth orbit with the sole assignment of taking pictures of the earth, while specialists on the ground analyze these images to extract valuable information from them. Activities as diverse as hurricane tracking and prospecting for new sources of copper are now undertaken by people who study pictures in air-conditioned offices. At this moment, electronics-laden probes are heading deeper and deeper into space, dutifully sending back the pictures they are taking on their tours. And although the two Viking landers that landed on Mars during the Bicentennial summer failed to find life there, they were most successful in transmitting crisp pictures of the planet. They were so efficient at this job that by the end of the summer, newspaper pictures from Mars had become as routine as those of Bicentennial parades and shopping center openings.

Despite all this, however, space photography is seldom thought of as a separate activity that can be appreciated on its own. There has never been a major gallery or museum exhibition of space photography, and only a few books have been published on the subject which, for the most part, have focused on a single aspect of space photography. The reason for this is that the pictures have been so useful that there has been little time or inclination to consider them for their aesthetic interest—to sit back and enjoy them. Even in the hands of editors at *Life* or *National Geographic Magazine,* the pictures were selected to tell a story or illustrate a "first" rather than to stand on their own as images or fine photographs.

The purpose of this book is to tell the story of space photography and to show off some of its best examples. The story tells how the space photography effort began and developed. It dwells on what went on behind the scenes, showing how certain key people created it and insured that it would be anything but routine. The story has been underplayed in the reports and press releases put out as part of the official record, but it is nonetheless rich and colorful.

The photos have been selected to give an overview of American space photography. A number of those that appear here have never been published before; others have appeared only in government reports and technical journals; and some are classics which you will probably recognize, but which had to be included because of their importance. (Some of these in the latter category have had their widest circulation through newspapers and television; these are media that, for technical reasons, cannot show them off to their best advantage.)

No formal criteria were set for picking the pictures, rather they were simply chosen because the author found them stirring and revealing. Undoubtedly, another person looking through the same collections would have made other choices—just as two museum curators would use different prints in a show of contemporary woodcuts. In short, it was a subjective process which will give the next book on space photography a much different look from this one.

First, the story.

To start, one could go all the way back to the famous French portrait photographer, Félix Tournachon, who went by the single name of Nadar. He pioneered the concept of aerial photography when he started making photographic balloon ascents in 1858. Or, for that matter, one could go back to pre-World War I Europe and the German, Alfred Maul, who was the first man to put a camera into a rocket and to lift it to a significant altitude (2,600 feet). Or, more recently, there are the photos taken by American sounding rockets shot from the New Mexico desert at regular intervals from 1946 through the 1950s. Since these rockets took pictures from altitudes as high as 158 miles and "space" is generally defined as existing above an altitude of 50 miles, this would seem to be the true beginning of space photography. I have chosen, however, to begin at another point, which seems to be the moment when the realization was first made that space photography would be something truly important and not just a technical curiosity.

For Want of a Thesis

In 1953, before there was Sputnik or NASA, a physicist named S. Fred Singer began talking about a pet idea of his for which he created the imaginative acronym MOUSE—Minimal Orbital Unmanned Satellite of Earth. The MOUSE would orbit the earth and radio back images that would show the world's weather in addition to such things as ice and snow cover on the ground. Although many of Singer's fellow scientists doubted that such a futuristic vehicle could produce pictures with sharp enough resolution to tell earthlings anything of much value, others were more optimistic. One of the most optimistic persons was the late Harry Wexler, who was the chief scientist at the US Weather Bureau. Wexler soon proposed a version of Singer's MOUSE that would send back television images of the planet, but his proposal was deemed premature and quickly shelved.

The idea was suddenly revived in the wake of Sputnik, and in 1958 the Pentagon's Advanced Research Projects Agency began working on it. In April of the following year the project was, for the most part, taken over by the new civilian Space Agency, which gave it a high priority. The first weather satellite, no longer MOUSE but TIROS-1—Television and Infrared Observation Satellite—was put into orbit in 1960.

Its significance was immediate in that, for the first time in history, humans were given a synoptic view of the weather. All at once the symbols and squiggly lines of the textbooks and weather charts came alive as storms were charted and fronts rendered graphic. As was to be the case with later photographic efforts from space, there was more detail in the first photographs than had been anticipated. The results of TIROS-1 surprised the experts when, for example, small ice formations on gulfs and bays could be seen clearly in the absence of clouds. It was also apparent that we could increase the warning time for severe weather, especially that coming in from the sea. Just nine days after the first launch, American weather analysts were able to give their counterparts in the Australian weather service the exact location of a typhoon located 800 miles east of Brisbane. TIROS-1 operated for 79 days and acquired some 20,000 photos in the process.

Within weeks of that first launch, NASA, the Commerce Department (which includes the Weather Bureau), and other interested government agencies began mapping out a plan for continuous worldwide satellite coverage. President Kennedy supported the idea and was able to get Congressional approval of the plan by the end of 1961.

The importance of TIROS-1 transcended the birth and subsequent growth of the weather satellite program because it was the first clear demonstration of the importance of space imagery. The significance of those first TIROS pictures was driven home by a small event—the choice of a topic for a doctoral thesis—with major consequences.

In 1962, Paul Merifield, a UCLA student who had just completed his master's degree in geology, happened to stop in at the office of Professor John Crowell to discuss ideas for a Ph.D. thesis. Crowell, who had just seen a batch of TIROS images for the first time, told Merifield that it might be a good idea to see if such pictures could be used to learn more about geology.

Merifield liked the idea and began working on it. In 1962, he made contact with Dr. Paul D. Lowman, Jr., a NASA geologist, to ask him for leads to other photographs that might help him with his thesis.

Lowman was only vaguely familiar with, and not very interested in, the pictures taken from the early Mercury capsules which in 1960 and 1961 had carried automatic 70 mm Maurer cameras programmed to take time-lapse sequences. These missions, which included both manned and unmanned trials, had brought back a few good pictures, but the results were generally uneven and unimportant. Some were never seen, as in the case of Virgil "Gus" Grissom's July, 1961 Liberty Bell 7 flight, in which the camera sank to the bottom of the Atlantic with the spacecraft just as the astronaut escaped. By all accounts, photography was given very minor consideration on these early flights, and there were good reasons for this. For one, the object of these missions was to gain an initial mastery of manned spaceflight, and everything else, including taking pictures, was considered secondary. Also, few people believed that such photos would be of any value. This belief was actually bolstered by some early studies that had concluded that it would be impossible to take photographs outside the earth's atmosphere.

What was more exciting than the automatic images, however, were the pictures that John Glenn had taken from his Friendship 7 spacecraft. Shortly before Merifield made contact with Lowman, Glenn had decided that he wanted to take some shots of earth as part of the record of his historic flight. He obtained an Ansco Autoset 35 mm camera and some Kodak color negative film, and during the mission in which he became the first American to go into earth orbit, he found the time to take thirty-eight photos. The Glenn pictures confirmed what had been suggested by some of the earlier robot shots, especially the few that had been taken of the Western Sahara by the unmanned Mercury 4: good, clear, and revealing photographs of the earth could be taken from space. One of the best of the lot was a very clear, very blue shot taken as Glenn crossed the Gulf of Mexico showing the Florida peninsula from its east to west coast. What is more, he had accomplished this photographic feat without special preparation on a tightly scheduled pi-

John Glenn's Ansco, the first hand-held camera in space.

oneering mission, encumbered by a helmet, heavy gloves, and other garb he could not remove. (The camera had been slightly modified to include a pistol grip, oversized film advance that could be worked with gloves on, and a viewfinder that allowed him to aim the camera with his helmet on).

As Merifield and Lowman discussed the Glenn pictures and the Mercury 4 pictures (which Lowman had not seen until the young doctoral student brought them to his attention), Merifield began pushing the idea of trying to get the next man in orbit to take pictures of the earth that would have scientific value for geologists and other specialists rather than allowing him to snap away at what struck his fancy. Lowman was persuaded and attempted to obtain a formal photographic plan for the next mission, which was to be Scott Carpenter's Mercury 7 on May 24, 1962. As the mission was already heavily booked with tasks for Carpenter to perform, the request was turned down, but Lowman did send a note to the astronaut asking *if* he did have time for photography, could he try to shoot some of the areas of the world that were included on a list. Carpenter was outfitted with a Robot Recorder hand-held 35 mm camera which had been selected because of a large aperture (f/0.95) that would make it effective in low-light situations. In all, Carpenter took two hundred photographs, which one of the NASA's top photographic experts, Richard Underwood, charitably termed "different." He captured on film such things as reflections on the capsule window, debris from the launch vehicle, ice crystals, and more that was of little value to people like Merifield and Lowman. Today Lowman says that Carpenter blew it photographically, but that it really was not the astronaut's fault since his schedule had been so overloaded that he even overshot his splashdown point by two hundred fifty miles.

In preparation for Wally Schirra's October, 1962 Mercury 8 mission, however, Lowman was permitted to brief the astronaut and to give him a photo plan. The outline for the briefing, which is still in Lowman's files, was both simple and specific. It reads in part as follows:

1. Give first priority to photos of the United States. The topography and geology are pretty well mapped, so we can use these photos as control.

2. Photographs of any land area are of some geologic interest; take advantage of any opportunities.

3. Record time, location, and film on tape.

4. Aim the camera down as much as possible.

5. Try to get some comparison photos in BW (black and white) and color of the same area.

6. The following areas or features are of particular interest, either for photographing or to look at:

First orbit—southern Algeria, 22 m, possible impact crater; East Africa, 30–33 m, Rift Valley, volcanoes.

Second orbit—Ghana, 1h 56–57 m, Bosumtwi crater, known impact feature, occupied by 5 mile diameter lake.

And so forth through six orbits.

There were high hopes that this mission would prove to be a photographic bonanza. Schirra was an avid amateur photographer who had been carefully briefed and had more time for picture taking than the harried Carpenter. Unfortunately, the pictures that came back were lousy, with most falling into one of two categories: overexposed and very overexposed. Schirra had pointed his camera at the right places on the ground, but had taken his exposure readings on the sky.

One of the early Hasselblad 500C models modified for use in space.

Yet there was, no pun intended, a bright side to the story. The Schirra flight established the camera that was to become the mainstay of the astronaut-photographer throughout the Mercury, Gemini, Apollo, and Skylab missions. NASA had originally intended to give Schirra a 35 mm camera, either another Robot Recorder or a Leica, but Schirra wanted to use his own favorite, a Hasselblad. As photo expert Underwood recalls, "In those days, as far as NASA was concerned the astronauts could walk on water. Schirra had a tantrum about the camera and it was decided to get him a Hasselblad." A Hasselblad 500C was bought off-the-shelf at a retail camera store and, like earlier cameras, specially modified for the space environment. Chrome surfaces that could reflect sunlight and cause eye damage were blackened, the synthetic leatherette was stripped off the body because technicians feared it might emit gas in the vacuum of space and make Schirra ill, and the viewfinder was removed lest it shatter accidentally and send glass flying around the capsule. Even though the pictures taken with the first orbiting Hasselblad were disappointing, NASA recognized that the versatile, large-format camera was right for space photography. Among other things, it featured interchangeable lenses and film magazines to accommodate, for instance, the quick change from color to black and white.

Finally, on the ninth Mercury mission in May, 1963, L. Gordon Cooper put it all together. When he asked the inevitable astronaut's question, "How did the pictures come out?", the answer was, "fantastic." Because of those pictures and others he took on a later Gemini mission, Cooper gained the reputation as the best of the space photographers—"Almost a professional," says Les Gaver, who is in charge of photography at NASA headquarters in Washington. "This was the big breakthrough," says Lowman, who had briefed Cooper along with Schirra, "because these made it clear that the pictures were not only good but useful as well." By this time, Lowman was in charge of evaluating the pictures, and when the developed transparencies were given to him, he was immedi-

ately drawn to frame 22—a picture Cooper had taken over Tibet. The picture was most revealing in that it showed the clearest geological structures. At first, Lowman had a hard time identifying exactly what part of Tibet it showed. After some research, he identified it as the Tibetan Plateau, an area that had never been mapped and about whose geography and geology practically nothing was known. Using frame 22 and a plotting table, Lowman was able, in a short period of time, to map this area which had previously been a blank spot on existing maps of Tibet. What is more, the map was detailed and sophisticated, as folds, domes, glacier lines, and snow-covered highlands were charted accurately for the first time. Although at the time the event attracted little attention outside the world of the earth sciences, it was a key moment in the development of space photography. Not only did we have the first of many maps made from space, but, outside of meteorology, the first practical earthly benefit from space photography had been realized.

One of Cooper's views. This is of the Himalayas at the border area of India, Nepal, and Tibet.

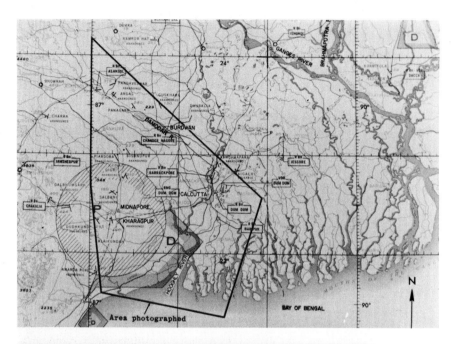

This Cooper photo of a portion of India is shown with a map of the same area.

Four months after Cooper returned with his photographs, the summary report of the mission was published. In the report, Lowman made a list of the potential uses of space photographs of the earth as foretold in Cooper's frames: "(1) geologic reconnaissance, (2) topographic mapping, (3) forest mapping, (4) icepack and iceberg monitoring, (5) supplemental weather observations, and (6) mapping of near-surface ocean currents." He added, "In addition, experience in interpreting such photographs will prove useful in interpreting similar photographs of the planets when they become available."

Cooper's was the last Mercury mission, and manned space photography moved to the two-astronaut Gemini missions, of which there were ten. On these missions, more than 2,400 photos were taken which included not only photos of the earth but also recorded docking maneuvers, space walks, and spacecraft interiors. There was still an unevenness in the photos, but many were supurb, and they were coming back in greater quantity as the astronauts and those who directed them on the ground were learning.

As the early photographs of the earth were studied more carefully and as more returned from the Apollo program, the importance of this kind of image continued to grow. Specifically, the excitement over the broad-brush geological information derived from the early earth photographs was real, but it was nothing when compared to that which took hold as the experts began to pull out remarkably detailed findings, many of which were totally unexpected. Gemini 4 photos taken in 1965 revealed hitherto unnoticed clues to sources of oil and gas in North Africa. Writing about a series of pictures taken from the same Gemini vehicle, former Secretary of the Interior Stewart L. Udall observed, "In just one pass, the Gemini astronauts photographed 80 percent of Peru; it took just three minutes. The scientists who have seen this mosaic consider it to be superior to any available map of the region in terms of information conveyed. One can see the gross patterns of land use, distribution of snow, the levels of the lakes, geologic features of possible economic significance—at a single glance."

Improved mapping from space was not just useful for lesser developed lands with vast wilderness areas: Gemini 5 and 7 pictures of Cape Kennedy revealed the embarrassing fact that even the most current maps of the area did not show a number of new roads and man-made features.

Other Gemini and Apollo photographs were used to discover an unmapped volcanic field in northern Mexico and to find a potentially major copper lode along the Arizona–New Mexico border. Theories about sedimentation in North American rivers were confirmed in living color, and several earthquake fault lines which had long avoided detection finally came into focus. Some details astonished even those who were most optimistic about the potential value of photographing the earth from space, such as when a photo taken by one man in orbit revealed another man illegally dredging oysters in Galveston Bay.

Probably, all of this would have happened even if Merifield had not been looking for a provocative thesis topic and in the process goaded Lowman, but it would have taken longer. To bring the story of the thesis full circle, in 1970 Lowman was very excited about some new pictures of the San Andreas fault, and he took them to the leading expert on the fault at the University of California, Santa Barbara. After marveling at the pictures, the expert leaned back in his chair and told Lowman, who had never heard the story before, that ten years earlier when he was at UCLA, he had suggested to a young student that he might find something of value in space photography. The expert, of course, was John Crowell, and the student was Merifield.

3

Good Shots

If they are not the best space photographs—although some think they are—they are certainly the most famous. The photos in question are, of course, those taken by the first human beings to touch the surface of a sphere other than the earth. In order for two members of the crew of Apollo 11 to get to the position where those pictures could be taken, much was done in advance. The story of the buildup to the first lunar landing is well known and does not bear repeating here, but the lesser-known photographic history of that endeavor does.

The first attempt to propel a man-made object to the moon took place in 1958 when the US Air Force aimed a rocket at it which proceeded to explode moments after take-off. It was not until October of the following year that photography entered the picture. It was a stunning debut. The Soviet Luna 3 unmanned probe not only photographed the moon, but it also radioed back crude images of its far side which had never been revealed to humans before. Some ardent nationalists in the US, obviously still reeling from Sputnik and the first unmanned crash landing on the moon by the Soviet Luna the previous month, called the pictures fakes, which they were not.

Meanwhile the US had decided to take a different approach in its effort to photograph the moon. The Ranger probes, which were intended to crash into the moon, would carry a special array of six television cameras, each of which would send back an image every 2.5 seconds during the period just before it slammed into the lunar surface. The early part of the Ranger effort was plagued with failure, so it was not until the Ranger 6 mission that it looked as if the US was going to have its first close-ups of the moon. Unfortunately, that perfect shot went sour in the last hour of flight when the cameras would not switch on due to a short in the system. Then, finally, in mid-1964, almost five years after the Luna 3 success, Ranger 7 shot back a collection of more than 4,000 televised stills before it crashed. These and those transmitted by the next two Rangers, which produced another 12,000 or so pictures, were so clear and detailed that astronomers said that some had ten times the resolution that could be achieved with the best telescopes on earth.

NASA, however, had precious little time to pride itself on the photographic success of the Rangers because at the beginning of 1966, the Soviet Luna 9 began transmitting. That craft had made the first soft lunar landing and was sending back pictures from the surface of the moon. Just a few months later, America's Surveyor 1 made a simi-

Edward H. White II operating in space.

lar soft landing. It was so prolific a robot photographer that it produced 11,000 pictures in six weeks. Astronomers and geologists had a field day with the pictures, and they will still be using them years from now to support theories and make specific discoveries. At the time, however, all the specific scientific considerations were secondary to one major finding: humans could go to the moon and survive. It was not until Luna 9 began sending back pictures, for instance, that there was detailed proof that the crust of the moon was not tenuous, as some had believed, and could indeed support men and landing vehicles.

The manned spaceflight program was developing quickly, as the bulk of these pictures were coming back from the probes and landers. The ground-breaking Project Mercury had given way to the Gemini series of two-man missions. During the ten Gemini missions, the United States tested and practiced those procedures that would be needed for the longer and more complicated Apollo missions to the moon. The Gemini missions lasted as long as two weeks and gave the astronauts the practice they needed at reentry and landing methods and rendezvousing and docking with other vehicles.

Photography had become a major element of the Gemini program, and constant improvements were being made in both the equipment and the photographic training of the astronauts who were told not only what to photograph but also how. Houston's Photographic Technology Laboratory even encouraged them to practice with their Hasselblads during off-duty hours. One technical development which began in the Mercury program but was refined in the Gemini program was the use of thin polyester Kodak films so that a large number of exposures could be made with one film magazine. This was important because space was at a premium in the small capsules, and NASA wanted to keep the number of loose items to a minimum. Eventually, up to two hundred exposures of 70 mm film were crammed into one specially built magazine which was a great improvement over the twelve exposures of roll film that fit in the commercial magazines for the Hasselblad.

The photographic highlights of the Gemini program included:

Gemini 4 (*June 3–7, 1965*)—James A. McDivitt takes pictures of Edward H. White II during his first American space walk. McDivitt's sharp photographs are not only of historic importance, but they are still widely regarded as the best ever taken of a man in space. *National Geographic Magazine,* a fair judge of color photography, went so far as to call them "some of the most breathtaking color photographs ever made." Looking back at them now after their news value has long faded, they are still spectacular and imply an even greater mastery of space than the many photographs made on and around the moon.

In some of the pictures, White can be seen carrying a camera, which was a Zeiss Contarflex used to photograph the outside of the Gemini vehicle to see if any damage had occurred during launch.

Gemini 5 (*August 21–29, 1965*)—Cooper and Charles Conrad, Jr., came back with a sensational batch of earth photos that mirrored a spontaneous exclamation that Conrad blurted out to ground control as he took in the earth view, "So vast, so beautiful, so overpowering. . . ."

Gemini 6 and Gemini 7 (*December 4–18, 1965*)—History's first space rendezvous replete with some awesome pictures of the event.

Gemini 8 (*March 16, 1966*)—The flight in which Neil Armstrong and David Scott accomplished the first docking in space with an unmanned Agena target vehicle. The terrifying yawing and rolling of the manned capsule during and after the short docking did not prevent the astronauts from getting a few good photographs of the event.

Gemini 9 (*June 3–6, 1966*)—An attempted docking that had to be canceled because the large protective shroud on the unmanned target vehicle did not fall away on schedule. The photographs were clear enough to be used later by NASA to figure out why the shroud did not shake loose. Because of this problem, the pictures of the target vehicle are especially memorable. The pesky shroud hung on in such a way that it looked like a set of mammoth jaws attached to a sinister space beast. Astronaut Thomas P. Stafford aptly called it "the angry alligator." The flight also marked the successful debut of a new space camera, the Hasselblad SWC, with a sweeping 90 degree angle of view.

Gemini 10 (*July 18–21, 1966*)—While Michael Collins was working outside of his spacecraft during this rendezvous and docking mission, he lost control of his camera, which had been attached to his space suit. Despite efforts to get it back, it sailed off into space and into orbit around the earth where it remains today. It was an accident that produced a public relations coup that even the most imaginative corporate publicist would have been hard pressed to duplicate. The Hasselblad company now had its own satellite. (Other Hasselblads have been left in space. A total of ten of them are on the moon, having been left by astronauts who had to lessen the weight of the return voyage.) The crews of Geminis 10, 11, and 12 all brought back good photographs.

Meanwhile, toward the end of the Gemini series, the first of an important set of five unmanned Lunar Orbiters was sent to the moon to finish the work the Rangers and Surveyors had started. These were photographic vehicles that featured rather conventional automatic cameras and a Kodak-engineered automated dark room that processed the film. The pictures were then sent along to be electronically scanned, turned into a series of electric impulses, and radioed back to earth where they were converted back into pictures. The Lunar Orbiters sent back some 1,600 photos which served to gather new information on the moon's surface so that NASA could begin the process of selecting sites for astronaut landings.

OPPOSITE: Mosaic of the front side of the moon from Lunar Orbiter images.

These photographic robots sent back not only a staggering amount of detailed new information about the moon, but also some very important individual photographs of general interest. One, a picture taken on August 23, 1966, showed the lunar surface in the foreground with the half-lit earth hanging above it. It was the first view humans had of their planet from the moon. Two months later Orbiter 2 took an unplanned test shot which NASA officials called the picture of the year, and some zealous newspaper editors termed it the picture of the century. It was a remarkably detailed and clear view of the lunar landscape looking out across the crater Copernicus. Although this picture has been pretty much forgotten today, it and others like it from later Orbiters had a great impact at the time. As Arthur C. Clarke explains in his book, *The Promise of Space,* "These photographs were of great psychological as well as scientific importance, for the Rangers, Lunas, and Surveyors had begun to give the impression that the Moon was a somewhat dull, flat and uninteresting place. But now the image was beginning to emerge of a world with landscapes as dramatic as any on Earth. . . ." Orbiter 4 was able to take a series of pictures of the moon's near side which were fitted together on earth to give us what was the best image of the full lunar disc up to that time. The complete mosiac created was 40 by 45 feet in size.

By early 1968, the combined efforts of the Ranger, Surveyor, and Lunar Orbiter projects had produced a collection of more than 100,000 clear photographs of the moon.

The tragic fire that killed the three Apollo astronauts in January, 1967 caused the program's flight schedule to be delayed for almost two years while equipment and procedures were restudied and tightened up for extra safety. This included details so small as the electric film drives on the cameras which had to be redesigned so they would operate in a high oxygen area without any danger of sparking an explosion or fire. When the flight program started up again with Apollo 7 at the end of 1968, the major concern was, for obvious reasons, the operation of the spacecraft itself. There were only two scientific experiments assigned to the crew; they were terrain photography and weather photography—an early indication of the importance that photography was to play in the Apollo program.

The first manned flight to the moon was Apollo 8, which circled it ten times in December, 1968 before returning. In strictly utilitarian terms, this was the most important photography yet accomplished by man in space because one of the prime functions of the mission was finally to locate the most suitable sites for the first landing which was to come less than a year later. In addition, some classic images were taken of the earth from the moon, of the full earth taken midway between the earth and the moon, and of the back side of the moon. One of the best pictorial sequences of this or of any other flight before or after was that of a bright, blue-marbled earth rising gradually over the barren lunar surface set

against the deep black of space. This famous "earthrise" series was almost not taken. Frank Borman, the man in command, saw the beginning of the earthrise and asked William Anders, the crew member in charge of photography, to get some pictures of it, but he refused, pointing out that it was not in his schedule of assignments. Borman grabbed the camera from Anders and took the remarkable pictures himself.

Apollo 9, the spacecraft sent into earth orbit to test the spider-like lunar lander in March, 1969, contained a camera-happy crew of three who ended up taking more than 3,000 photographs, which was more than had been taken in all of the Gemini flights put together. At one point when all three crewmen had cameras in their hands, Russell Schweickart was prompted to report to the controllers in Houston, "Now we're all taking pictures of everybody taking pictures." In this case, quality came with quantity in some brilliant pictures of a space walk, the earth, the lunar and command modules, and the men inside. This flight carried a cluster of four Has-

One of Frank Borman's famous "earthrise" photographs.

ABOVE: Portrait of the first lunar photographer. OPPOSITE: Aldrin walking near the lunar module—perhaps the most famous of all space photographs.

selblad 500ELs, a new model which had made its debut on Apollo 7, which were fitted together to get views of the same areas on earth simultaneously with different film and filter combinations. This was done to obtain the kind of information that can be discovered as images taken in different portions of the spectrum are examined for special information. An infrared photo taken on this flight, for instance, showed that "thin" layers of snow show up green from space, while "thick" snow appears in blue. Incidentally, this was the first flight for which extra fuel was provided so that the crew could maneuver the spacecraft to get the best pictures.

Apollo 10 came next (much like Apollo 8 save for a very tense period during which the lunar module gyrated violently with two astronauts aboard), and the lunar landing would be attempted on the next mission. For an event as monumental as the first moon

landing, special photographic preparations were in order. Long before the Apollo 11 flight, work had begun on the special lunar cameras which had to meet rigid specifications regarding shock, temperature, solar radiation, and moisture. One of these cameras was the Hasselblad Lunar Data Camera, and the other was the Apollo Lunar Surface Data Camera (ALSDC), an ingenious cane-like device constructed by Eastman Kodak which was to be used by the astronauts to take close-up pictures of the undisturbed lunar surface in three dimensions. Stereoscopic pairs were to be made which could later be viewed by scientists on the ground through a viewer much like the Victorian parlor stereoscope. Both cameras would have silvered surfaces to reflect heat and radiation, which cause severe temperature variations within them, a departure from the blackened cameras used up to this point.

There was extensive preparation for the actual taking of the pictures. As Dick Underwood of the Photographic Technology Division at Houston recalls, "The Lunar Orbiters gave us a pretty good idea of how the moon reflects light, and then we got even more information on this when we got the Apollo 8 photos. By then we were able to predict very accurately how to set the cameras. Our major concern was the sun because there weren't going to be any obstructing clouds to worry about and we knew that the pictures would be clear because of the absence of atmosphere."

The astronauts were given detailed instructions and practiced on a special set, a simulated lunar landscape, in Houston which approximated the light conditions they would encounter on the moon. Actual rolls of film were shot and developed so they could get a feel for it. There were other details that had to be attended to as well, such as wiring the American flag so that it would "wave" on the windless lunar surface—a Hollywood touch that was excusable since a limp flag would have been most unphotogenic.

When the lunar lander Eagle touched down in the Sea of Tranquility on July 20, 1969, the crew's initial concern was to get the television camera into operation so that the world could witness the historic event. Soon a lot of still photographs were being taken by Neil Armstrong; they included everything from tourist-like shots of Edwin Aldrin posing by the flag to rock shots that only a geologist could love. The most memorable photo had to be a full-length picture of Aldrin looking straight at the camera with his special gold-plated face visor (designed to protect him from the unfiltered rays of the sun) reflecting both Armstrong and the lunar module itself. In their own humble way, the photographs of footprints in the lunar dust were stirring—even powerful—as they represented, however abstractly, the first human contact with another body in the universe.

On subsequent lunar landings, the astronauts used up tremendous amounts of film recording and mapping the moon in much more detail. The crew of Apollo 15 alone exposed more than two miles of film during its summer of 1971 mission. Among other things, there were ultraviolet and infrared photography of the moon, extensive photographic mapping, pictures of the solar corona, more stereoscopic photography, and, on the Apollo 12 mission of November, 1969, pictures of the long-silent Surveyor 3, which had not been seen since it was launched in April, 1967.

For the manned flights of the mid-1970s, the three Skylab long-duration missions, and the US–Soviet Apollo–Soyuz linkup, there were many productive photographic activities, including the use of Skylab photographic telescopes to obtain a massive collection of images of the sun and many more photographs of the earth. On the final Skylab mission, which lasted for 84 days, one hour, and 16 minutes (spanning the period from November, 1973 to February, 1974), some 75,000 pictures were taken of the sun and 20,000 of the earth. Photography from manned spacecraft will get into full swing again shortly as the Space Shuttles go into operation in 1980 after a test period beginning in 1977.

4

The Weather Birds

The United States has successfully launched and orbited thirty-five weather satellites which have collectively produced millions of images. Between 1960 and 1970, some 1,750,000 images were sent back, and more are coming in daily. Over this period new equipment has been tested and refined, and vast improvements have been made in the quality of the pictures and the coverage made by individual satellites. Early spacecraft, which were able to view only 20 percent of the earth each day, have given way to vehicles which continuously photograph half the earth.

Along the way, there were a number of important firsts and interesting developments. The success of TIROS-1 was followed up by others in the series that made their own history. In 1961 TIROS-3 became the first satellite to discover a hurricane and to track it along a complex path. The eighth TIROS carried an improved new camera system that was able to transmit pictures to relatively inexpensive ground stations that were literally closet-sized. Small or poor nations could now have their own weather services if twenty thousand dollars could be spared to buy a receiver. Soon radio amateurs and electronics buffs got into the act and were rigging their own receiving stations with second-hand parts for less than five hundred dollars. In one day in 1965, TIROS-9 cranked out 480 pictures of the earth made during 12 orbits. The pictures were pasted together to create the first complete view of the world's weather. TIROS-9 was able to do this because, unlike earlier models, it rolled like a wheel in orbit with a camera on either side of the wheel that allowed it to photograph more of the earth on each pass. In addition, it had been placed in polar orbit—that is, a path that took it by the two poles—so that during daylight hours the sun was always behind the cameras which, as any Sunday snapshooter knows, is the best way to get a clear, well-lit photo.

The Nimbus experimental weather satellites which started going up in 1964 did their own pioneering. The first one carried a high-resolution infrared instrument that made cloud photography at night a reality, while Nimbus-3 used other infrared instruments to take temperature measurements in the atmosphere from space. These and other innovations tested on early Nimbus satellites were incorporated into the design of the ITOS (Improved TIROS Operational Satellite) spacecraft which took over from TIROS as the nation's "workhorse" weather satellite in 1970.*

---

* Weather satellite nicknames and acronyms can be very confusing. For instance, once an ITOS spacecraft is in orbit it becomes NOAA-1, NOAA-2,

TIROS-9 photomosaic of the world's weather.

Some important developments were not tied to single satellites. In 1964, for instance, the US and Soviet Union created a system by means of which they transmitted their satellite weather photos to each other on a daily basis. This electronic swapping of images was quickly dubbed "the cold line," a takeoff on the "hot line" crisis communications hookup between the White House and the Kremlin.

The list of advances goes on and on, but one more must be mentioned here. This is the development of the new geostationary weather satellites that move through space at the same rate as the earth turns, thereby allowing them to hover over the same point above the globe. A single spacecraft, called Synchronous Meteorological Satellite (SMS), can take one detailed, high-resolution pic-

and so on. NOAA stands for the National Oceanic and Atmospheric Administration, which operates them. Moreover, other satellites of the TIROS-type (called TOS for TIROS Operational Satellite, not to be confused with ITOS) which flew between 1966 and 1969 took the name ESSA-1, ESSA-2, and so on after launching. ESSA stands for the Environmental Science Services Administration, which is what NOAA (the agency, not the satellite) was called before the name was changed in 1971. Before the agency was ESSA or NOAA, it was known as the Weather Bureau, which was obviously too simple and direct a name to let stand.

ture of the two hemispheres every half hour. For pictures that show half the world, the resolution is truly remarkable: down to a half mile during the day and five miles at night. At present, geostationary satellites are stationed over each hemisphere, which means that we can get an updated photographic synopsis of the world's weather as often as forty-eight times a day—a major refinement of the art of meteorological photography.

Needless to say, the primary function of these satellites is to provide the information needed for more sophisticated and longer-range forecasts. Officials at NASA and NOAA are firmly convinced that the forecasting art has advanced significantly since the advent of weather satellites. Recently NOAA administrator Robert M. White summed up this position at a Nobel science symposium in Oslo, "Weather forecasts are now more accurate than ever before, and American meteorologists have been able to enlarge the period covered by their forecasts. Twenty years ago, meteorologists could not forecast the weather four or five days ahead with significant skill. Today they can do so." Some would argue that the general improvement has not been that great, but hardly anyone would deny the dramatic role these picture-taking spacecraft have had as disaster warning systems. Because of them, the day has passed in

Storm off New Zealand, a TIROS-7 image.

which a hurricane or tropical storm can bash undetected and unannounced into the North American coast. NOAA, in fact, brags that since 1965 no serious storm anywhere in the world has avoided a satellite mug shot. In 1972 when Hurricane Agnes was moving on its erratic and destructive course, some 90,000 residents of Wilkes-Barre, Pennsylvania were warned and safely evacuated before the city was virtually destroyed by flooding. And in April, 1974 when the US was hit with its worst tornado outbreak in modern history

(148 tornadoes in 13 states in less than 24 hours), there was advance warning. In both these cases (and in a number of others), the death toll would have certainly been much higher than the 118 who died from Agnes and the 300 tornado fatalities.

In other cases, ships distressed by heavy storms at sea have been radioed advice on how to get out of the storm by experts looking at pictures of the storm. Meanwhile, geostationary satellites have just taken on a new disaster warning role. A number of sensing devices on earth are now sending information to the satellites which, in turn, relay it back to the World Weather Building in Suitland, Maryland—all in a matter of seconds. These sensors have been placed in such isolated but crucial places as the headwaters of rivers (to measure water level), remote ocean locations outside shipping lanes (to sense the sea state), and mountain tops (to clock wind). The director of the National Environmental Satellite Service recently explained the usefulness of the scheme, "This means that when a water level indicator at the upper reaches of a river, for example, senses the river about to reach flood stage . . . this vital information can be flashed, via satellite, to those concerned with warning the populace downriver that they should begin to prepare for flood waters."

These pictures also have a number of less obvious uses. The Coast Guard and Civil Air Patrol study them to pinpoint areas where lost ships and planes are most likely to get into trouble because of bad weather—a technique that has proven its value by saving lives and reducing search costs. Commercial fishing interests in the Pacific are using them to locate cold, nutrient-rich areas where tuna and salmon are most likely to be found. Hydrologists extract information on snowfall and snowmelt from them, and environmentalists use them to monitor chlorophyll levels in lakes. Other scientists are using them to study long-term climate developments. For instance, images of North American snow cover have been watched closely for nine years by NOAA scientists who, as a result, now seriously question predictions that there is a trend toward harsher weather.

Other promising applications are in the developmental stage. Infrared weather images have been specially enhanced such that ground temperatures show up in discernible shades of gray, from black to white. This technique has been so well refined that readings in the 31–33 degree range can be spotted at a glance. This process could be of great importance to farmers, and especially to fruit growers, to let them know with certainty that the temperature is reaching the point at which they have to heat their groves artificially.

Still another project underway to gain greater benefits from the pictures is aimed at controlling locust plagues in Africa. It is being conducted jointly by the US and the UN's Food and Agriculture Organization which sees locust control as essential to the future of African agriculture. In this experiment, weather satellite pictures are used to locate evidence of rain in the North African desert re-

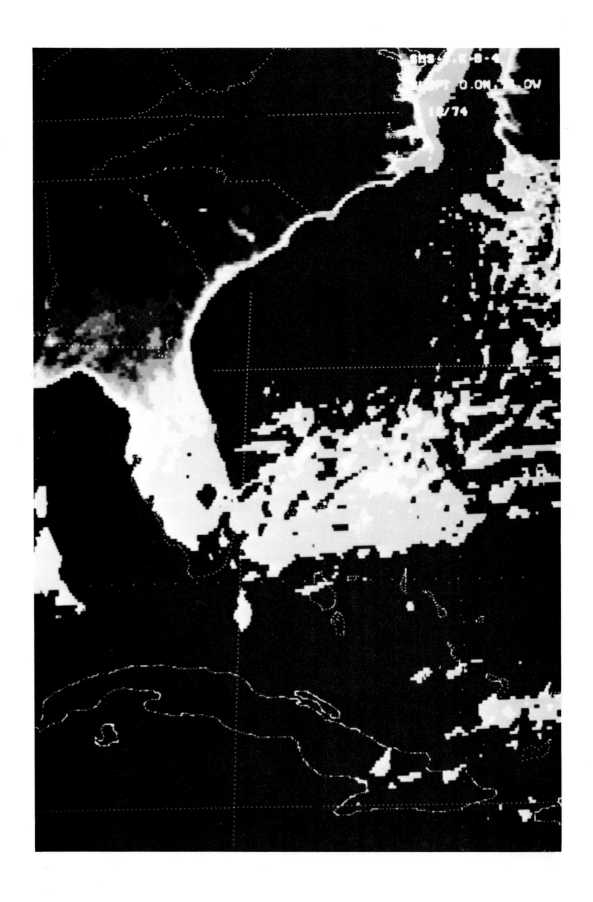

gion; these pictures are then compared with later earth images to see if the rain created any vegetation. Since these pockets of vegetation are essential to locust development, local teams on the ground are then sent to the area to kill the insects before they can become part of a devastating migratory swarm. If this system works, and early results have been quite promising, the project will be expanded to take in the entire twelve million square mile African locust zone.

The great usefulness of these images to experts is important, but how do they stand up as pictures?

Putting it bluntly, the pictures produced by the nation's flock of meteorological satellites lack the glamour generally associated with other types of photographs taken from earth orbit. For openers, they are normally only in black and white, can be quite repetitious, and are as plentiful as drugstore-processed snapshots of birthday parties. Millions of these images are already on file and crates of new ones are being added daily.

Despite this, these pictures sometimes have an appeal that extends far beyond their appeal to the scientists and technicians who dwell on their details. Occasionally there are spectacular shots such as those that depict the earth's weather at its most turbulent. For instance, it is awesome to look at a picture of a major portion of the globe and at one glance spot three hurricanes at play over the Atlantic Ocean. In a picture like this, usually shown as a 10 by 10-inch print, the earth is the size of a volley ball, and the hurricanes are wild-looking white swirls with pure white cores the size of marbles. It becomes even more dramatic when looked at in combination with pictures of the same area taken over a period of several days, which permits you to watch the three storms play to a finish with, say, two petering out at sea and the third crashing into the east coast of the United States.

In other pictures, we can watch forest fires, observe icebergs, or, cloud cover permitting, be hit by the shock of recognition that comes when we see that a synoptic image of northern Europe has precisely the same outline as a map of the area drawn by a human hand. It is a small thing, but it is still exciting to see with one's own eyes that, in this case, the real and the abstract are one and the same.

Finally, it must be pointed out that what is perhaps the single most important series of space photographs came out of a weather photography experiment. Their importance does not simply come from the consensus that they were good, which they were, but from what we were able to see for the first time. The first of these images was made on November 10, 1967 by a spacecraft in the Applications Technology Satellite series, ATS-3, which was testing a new color scan camera. The pictures are in color and show the earth for what it is: a finite ball standing alone in the void of space. We could at last see that our earth was indeed a planet—a pretty blue one shining vividly in a black vacuum. We could at once understand

OPPOSITE: Thermal map of the Florida area. The eight shades of gray in the northern part of the state represent varying temperatures from 16 to 31 degrees F.

31

The historic November 10, 1967 ATS-3 image of the world.

what Buckminster Fuller meant when he coined the term "Spaceship Earth," and we could see the fragile and perfectly round "Big Blue Marble" celebrated in the children's television show. It was what we all knew we would see, but couldn't see until the picture was made.

There had been partial pictures of the earth before, including the famous first blurry glimpse of the half-lit, distant globe taken from the moon by Lunar Orbiter, but these ATS pictures produced a deep impact by giving us the color, the detail, and, above all, the image of a planet standing alone in space. The white clouds, green vegetation, blue water, and brown arid lands were all there, and the detail was truly amazing. In an especially clear view that came down a week after the first one, there was a tiny dark spot at the bend of the west coast of South America. It was Lake Titicaca.

The image has been given to us again and again since 1967, and, in fact, it was very quickly reshot by Apollo astronauts who not only brought back the pictures in their film packs, but also told us about what it was like to actually eyeball this "other spacecraft" with its limited life-support system. And there were more dramatic views of the earth to come, such as the haunting Apollo 8 shot of the earth rising above the lunar landscape. Yet, for many, it is the first ATS images that will never be forgotten.

In 1948 the noted British astronomer and mathemetician Sir Fred Hoyle said, "Once a photograph of the Earth, taken from outside, is available—once the sheer isolation of the earth becomes plain, a new idea as powerful as any in history will be let loose." In 1970, during a speech in Houston, Hoyle reflected on his earlier prediction and those early earth images which had become universally known. He was not alone in his belief when he said:

> Well, we now have such a photograph, and I've been wondering how this old prediction stands up. Has any new idea in fact been let loose? It certainly has. You will have noticed how quite suddenly everybody has become seriously concerned to protect the natural environment. Where has this idea come from? You could say from biologists, conservationists and ecologists. But they have been saying the same things as they're saying now for many years. Previously they never got on base. Something new has happened to create a worldwide awareness of our planet as a unique and precious place. . . .

Meanwhile, at about the same time that these earth views were first coming back, an unusual, behind-the-scenes struggle was going on in Washington to determine how best to take the next step in earth-oriented space photography, which was to move from merely observing our small planet to learning more about caring for it. What went on was not only a fascinating political and scientific struggle in itself, but was one whose dynamic consequences we are just now beginning to realize. These consequences underscore what Margaret Mead had in mind when she said, "We are at a point in history where a proper attention to space, and especially near space . . . may be absolutely crucial in bringing this world together."

5

The Whole Earth Satellite

The photographs of the earth that astronauts were bringing back with them from earth orbit in the 1960s were eagerly studied by scientists on the ground, but there was a growing frustration among certain geologists and other specialists who wanted more photographs than the busy astronauts could take. What these people started talking about was a constantly updated photographic coverage of the whole earth from space that would be much more detailed than the synoptic images taken by weather satellites. As late as 1970, a leading government geologist pointed to the irony of the situation when he remarked, "Right now our collection of photographs of the moon are more uniformly comprehensive than those we have of the earth."

Moreover, this group did not just want more pictures, but pictures of a different kind, specifically, images taken in distinct bands of the light spectrum including the infrared. Use of such images which portray objects in "false color" had been shown to reveal information not apparent to the naked eye or to normal color films. Virtually every type of object under the sun has what is called a light signature or light signal. Just as snow, corn, a pine tree, an active volcano, and a geological fault have different signatures, so does young barley, mature barley, and diseased barley. By slicing up the spectrum, identification of these signatures becomes easier. Looking at objects in different lights also permits deeper probing (something that was learned in World War II with "false image" infrared film developed by Kodak to expose enemy camouflage from airborne cameras.) For instance, it is easier to "see through" clear water in the green portion of the spectrum, while the features of surface water show themselves best in infrared. In a variety of experiments, first with high-flying photo reconnaissance planes and later on Apollo 9 in 1969, it was shown that false color was highly revealing from high altitudes. Trees infested with insects, for instance, were pictured in blue against the reds of their healthy neighbors, and pictures of the ground in winter portrayed "thin" layers of snow in green and "thick" ones in blue.

The potential usefulness of this developing technology was apparent as scientists began talking about such things as detecting crop diseases, geological faults, and hidden sources of fresh water from the vantage point of space. The main question that remained among those who wanted to exploit the idea was how and when would a major space-based earth resources program get underway. As it turned out, that question was a major one which took a long time to answer.

In 1964 NASA sent a request to the US Geological Survey, an element of the Department of the Interior, asking it to join NASA in studies and experiments relating to earth resources imaging. The NASA plan called for experiments that would involve pictures taken from airplanes. Key officials of the Survey, especially its director, the late William T. Pecora, and senior geologist William A. Fisher, welcomed the experiments but felt they were not extensive enough. They were convinced that the next logical step was to move to an experimental, unmanned satellite that would be put into earth orbit with a collection of imaging devices. Fisher, who had been in charge of the Survey's efforts to learn more about the earth's geology from aircraft, argued that it would take some twenty years for planes to do what one satellite could do in less than three weeks: take pictures of the entire earth. Pecora and Fisher then convinced Interior Secretary Stewart Udall of the soundness of the idea, and he, in turn, backed a request asking NASA to put such a satellite into its plans for the near future. In addition to the request, detailed specifications were sent to NASA concerning how the satellite could be built.

The NASA high command, however, was definitely not interested in this kind of satellite and turned it down flatly. The major reason for this was that Administrator James Webb and others were determined to have earth resources work done by large orbiting stations staffed with astronauts and scientists—despite the fact that unmanned satellites had been proven to be efficient, reliable, and infinitely cheaper. But Webb and company were interested in insuring a major role for manned flight after the moon landings and felt that one good way to do so was to stake out certain earth orbiting jobs for humans.

What happened next was extraordinary. On September 21, 1966, the following statement was issued by the Department of the Interior:

> Project EROS was announced today by Secretary of the Interior Stewart L. Udall. EROS (Earth Resources Observation Satellites) is a program aimed at gathering facts about the natural resources of the earth from earth-orbiting satellites carrying remote sensing observation instruments.

The Department of the Interior had made the stunning announcement that it was going to start its own space program and send up satellites (the plural was used in the release), and the press picked it up from there and was soon providing additional details on EROS. *The Washington Post,* for example, was able to report that two EROS satellites would be launched by Thor-Delta rockets.

What the press did not understand, however, was that EROS was an imaginative and provocative hoax staged by the Department of the Interior to get NASA moving. Even the acronym, EROS, was calculated to goad the space policymakers on the other side of town. The press, the public, and certain members of Congress fell for the story even though Udall's department had neither the mandate nor the ability to start its own space program. It would not have been much less absurd if the Internal Revenue Service or the Food and Drug Administration had announced space programs of their own.

Of course, NASA was not taken in by the announcement. Nonetheless, it was surprised and angered by the audacious move and more determined than ever not to budge on the issue. The announcement, however, had brought the issue into the open, and the Department of the Interior was far from giving up on its campaign. Udall appealed to the National Academy of Sciences, which appointed a special study group to look into NASA's public claim that it did not have the available technology for such a satellite. That panel concluded that NASA was wrong because the technology was available. Next, the matter was brought to the attention of the House Science and Astronautics Committee, which investigated the issue and sided with the Department of the Interior and the National Academy of Sciences. The committee told NASA it would approve funds for the satellite if NASA asked for them.

Ultimately, the pressure (especially that building in Congress) was too much for NASA, and its 1970 budget contained a request for funds to study such a satellite, and the 1971 budget request included funds for the building of two satellites, the first of which would be launched in 1972. Once NASA made the decision to go ahead, it did an abrupt about face, and, like the Department of the Interior, its officials were soon giving speeches in which they told of the cornucopia of benefits which would result from NASA's Earth Resources Technology Satellites, a title that was soon shortened to ERTS. As it turned out, NASA did fly earth resources experiments on its manned Skylab missions in the 1970s.

The final plan called for the spacecraft to climb to an altitude of 560 miles, at which point it would shift into a longitudinal orbit taking it by the North and South Poles with each pass. On this course, all of the United States and most of the rest of the world would be seen and recorded by its lens every eighteen days. The orbits would be synchronized with the sun so that every area surveyed would be pictured with the sun shining at the same angle on each pass. On the ground three receiving stations were being readied to accept the images that would be transmitted.

The ERTS craft itself was built by General Electric. Its shape resembles a butterfly, and it weighs just over a ton. The prime photographic element for the vehicle is a multispectral scanner built by the Hughes Aircraft Co. (There is inescapable irony in the fact that the name of the world's most famous camera-shy recluse appears on what may be the world's most revealing piece of photographic equipment.) The Hughes scanner records the same scene simultaneously in the green, red, and infrared portions of the spectrum. In addition, the spacecraft was outfitted with three special television cameras which, like the scanner, take pictures in different portions of the spectrum. These cameras, made by RCA, pro-

Artist's conception of ERTS in orbit.

duce images that are nearly ten times sharper than those seen on a home television set.

Although the first satellites were to be termed "experimental," the term was misleading since the idea was to begin immediately applying ERTS information to real problems. Prior to the first launch, the Geological Survey's Fisher likened them to, of all things, the Metroliner. He explained, "There are two ways to conduct an experiment, which both the Metroliner and satellite are. To use the Metroliner as an example, you can either run it every day for people to use, as is being done, to find out how people really react to it, or you can use what I call the old-fashioned approach, which would call for running it every few weeks, paying people to ride it, and then studying the people. I think we're learning a lot more about the Metroliner by using it experimentally than by experimenting with it—and, of course, people are getting the benefit. . . ."

In the months just prior to the launching of the first satellite, there was much discussion of its merits. Officials of NASA and the Geological Survey were unified in their enthusiasm and issued a steady stream of press releases and reports that reported a number of earthly benefits were sure to accrue. Others were far from enthusiastic. Depending on which critic you talked to, the satellite images would either be so imprecise that they would be of little use in locating minerals and other earth resources, or so precise that they would invite the immediate overexploitation of natural resources. Dr. Simon Ramo, the vice-chairman of TRW Inc., was not alone in asking, "Can you imagine the opportunities for villany and plunder when the news leaks out?" Thoughtful legislators and scientists in the United States talked of the inevitable "land rape" from a space age Pandora's box, and a number of observers overseas agreed with several members of the British Parliament who termed the program "open economic espionage" on the part of the American government. Scenarios were discussed in which the industrialized nations and the multinational corporations would further impoverish the third world nations by gobbling up their most valuable resources. (There was real concern for American international exploitation despite the fact that the US had notified the United Nations in 1969 of its commitment to provide earth resources data for the whole world.) Still others contended that ERTS was an old-fashioned boondoggle—a glamorous set of public relations satellites sent up by NASA to produce handsome pictures of questionable scientific value.

ERTS-1 was launched on July 23, 1972, and within two days it was sending down its first pictures. Within weeks it was clear that, on the average, these pictures were excellent both in quality and in detail. They had definite limitations (coal veins, for instance, were too thin to be seen), but they were detailed enough to show floods, volcanoes, and earthquake fault and fracture lines; to chart the movement of glaciers and ice packs; and to pinpoint pollution sources. Specialists were excitedly reporting new clues to puzzles in their respective fields. Soon some intriguing anecdotes started making the rounds: An American hydrologist picked out a potentially productive site to drill for water in an arid location in Africa after looking at one picture for a few minutes. He then discovered that the same exact spot had already been picked for drilling after two years of costly survey work on the ground.

Criticism virtually disappeared as it became evident that the satellite was going to be extremely useful. The images were much more detailed than one group of critics had predicted, but not quite so revealing as others had predicted in the fear that they would touch off a plunderous rash of gold, silver, and petroleum rushes.

One of the most telling examples of this shift in opinion is evident in two articles by *The Washington Post*'s respected science writer Thomas O'Toole. The first article, "Research Satellite Has Its Limits," which appeared shortly before the first launch, was a catalog of the objections, worries, and second thoughts being expressed about the first two satellites. The gist of the article could not be missed: the program was one that was beginning to look as if it might create more problems than it solved. A year and some days later, after the first satellite had been in orbit for eight months, O'Toole wrote another article, entitled "Earth-Viewing

U.S. Satellite Proves Values," which opened with these lines:

When the space agency put its first Earth Resources Technology Satellite into orbit last July, the scientific community scorned the $200 million project as an adventure that would be best remembered for its waste.

Nothing has been further from the truth.

The windmill-shaped spacecraft has already charted most of America's croplands, its watersheds and even its pollution. It has found copper in Pakistan and oil in Alaska. It has identified all the major smoke plumes in Virginia, some of them unknown to the state's environmentalists. It made a geological map of Wyoming in one day, a feat that would have taken geologists 20 years.

Enthusiasm like O'Toole's was widespread. One was hard-pressed to find a congressman or senator who had a bad word to say about the system, and many were crowing about the immediate benefits to their states or regions in the pages of *The Congressional Record*. Some of the same scientists who were most cynical about what one of them once termed, "NASA's belated and ineffectual salute to the problems here on earth," were soon producing conference papers on discoveries they had made from a pile of ERTS images. NASA Administrator James C. Fletcher took a look at the satellite's performance before it had been in orbit for a year and proclaimed, "We're getting much more out of this program than anyone predicted." It was hard to find anyone willing to accuse him of overstatement. For its part, the press became infatuated with the new satellite, and it got rave reviews everywhere, from the Sunday supplements to *Fortune,* which said of it, "Some scientists liken the satellite's contribution to the invention of the microscope. This time the whole earth is under a microscope."

One very important factor in all of this was that the very groups that had worried most about the satellite's potential for exploiting the environment and the third world were finding their fears unjustified. Indeed, it was becoming apparent that the environmentalists and less-developed nations would benefit rather than be victimized by the new technology.

If anyone was being "exploited," it was the polluters, who were learning that their violations were much harder to hide or to downplay when they showed up clearly in a color image. Moreover, environmentalists were given something that was not fully appreciated until the pictures began showering down from orbit: an exact portrait of the whole earth as it was in July, 1972 (and every few weeks thereafter, clouds permitting) which had never existed before. The importance of this was that there was now, to use the environmentalist's own term, a "base line" against which to measure all future actions so that, for example, as strip mines etch lines on a region, nobody will ever again be able to minimize the effect of these scars with words when pictures prove the case to be otherwise.

ERTS-1 picture shows silt suspended in Delaware Bay.

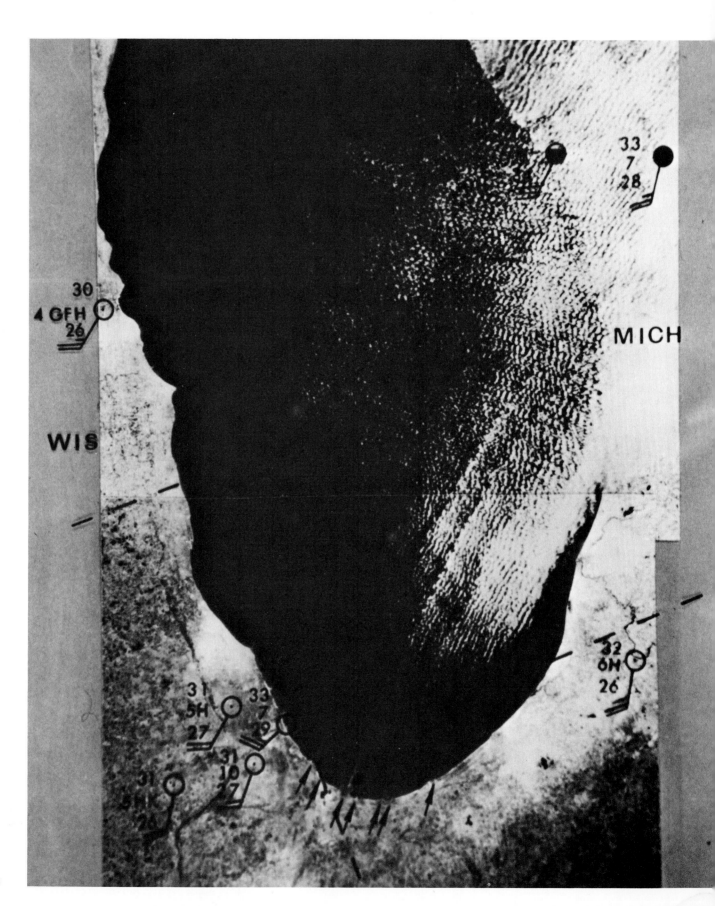

The United States government was true to its word that it would share its pictures with anyone in the world, nation or individual, who wanted them and has, in fact, worked to get as many nations involved as possible. The result has gone a long way to justify Arthur C. Clarke's oft-quoted remark, "It is the poor countries which must have space technology, it is the wealthy countries which may not need it. An ironic thought." By recent count some sixty nations were using the images on a regular basis, with a number reporting major findings from them. Of course, the big oil and mineral companies are looking at these images too, but that gives them no special advantage since even a poor nation with a good geologist working for it can see the same clues to new deposits.

Meanwhile, it is clear that nations other than the United States will continue to benefit. The United Nation's Food and Agriculture Organization (FAO) has announced that it will be using the satellites to prospect for new opportunities for food production. More than a half dozen nations are now in the process of acquiring their own ground stations so that they can directly receive and process their own images, and Canada has just decided to buy its second ground terminal.

The second satellite was put into orbit in early 1975, and shortly thereafter NASA headquarters decided to change the name of the two satellites from the guttural ERTS to the euphonious Landsat. ("I usually oppose changing names for public relations purposes," says one scientist associated with the program," but in this case it was justified because we were all getting tired of telling people we weren't clearing our throats when we talked about ERTS.") The first satellite, now Landsat 1, which had been built to last for a year, was still working when Landsat 2 went up, and both were doing well when this book was written in early 1977. Landsat 3 is scheduled to join the flock at about the time that this book first appears in the fall of 1977. The third satellite will produce images with twice the resolution of the first two.

It is one thing to list the general uses to which Landsat imagery is being applied, but quite another to get down to specifics. The specific examples underscore the remarkable utility of what is fast being recognized as history's most ambitious attempt to exploit photographic technology. Here is but a score of examples from the increasingly thick file of Landsat success stories.

● The leader of an Egyptian–American team which has been studying Landsat images since 1972 reported, in the summer of 1976, that the two satellites had already revealed previously unknown sources of water, oil, uranium, and other minerals in the Sahara and Sinai Deserts. In addition, team leader Ahmed Abdul Hady made the stunning revelation that there was evidence of enough water in the Sinai "to turn most of it green." These Egyptian findings explain why Landsat images have become such a hot commodity in the Middle East. *Newsweek* reported recently that nations in this part of the world are not only buying every conceivable kind of

OPPOSITE: Pollution plumes as light white stripes on this image of Lake Michigan. (See arrows at the south end of the lake.)

enhancing and processing equipment that appears on the market but are seriously talking about launching their own Landsat-type satellite in the future.

● The Texas Water Development Board is using the satellite images to generate monthly maps to locate and analyze playas, short-lived lakes caused by rainstorms. Such mapping is important in utilizing the water in the playas most efficiently for farm irrigation.

● The US Navy has used daily Landsat pictures of Antarctica to pick out small cracks and openings in the ice pack so that it could map out a course to get a National Science Foundation ship into remote Pine Island Bay. This allowed the ship, which carried supplies for a research expedition, to locate 1,200 miles closer to the expedition site than would have been possible without the satellite pictures.

● In the spring of 1975 when heavy spring floods began in Louisiana, Governor Edwin Edwards asked NASA to supply the state with the latest images on a priority basis. With the aid of a computer, the pictures were converted into a complete inventory of flood damage within two weeks. Using traditional methods, it would have taken several months to complete the inventory and would have required thousands of photos taken from aircraft.

● For decades archaeologists have been trying to figure out the function of a system of roadways built by the Anasazi, ancient Pueblo Indians, in northwestern New Mexico. Remaining fragments of the roadbed indicate that there were some 400 miles of road in the original system. Because of synoptic Landsat images of the area, a pair of scholars now reports that the reason for the roadways has become "instantly apparent." They were built by the Indians to gain access to forests for food and wood and to other areas for the raw materials needed to make pottery and stone tools.

● University of Vermont scientists have used Landsat images to identify a major pollution source in Lake Champlain caused by a paper mill in the state of New York. The imagery was accepted as evidence by the Supreme Court in Vermont's case (later settled out of court) against the mill and New York State. This was one of the first state-against-state pollution suits accepted by the Supreme Court.

● Commercial publishers have begun to benefit from the photographs. For instance, forty-five images of Baja California were combined with existing highway maps in *The Baja Book*, creating the first complete set of maps of the area. In the same vein, Kistler Graphics of Colorado has used satellite photos to construct a 3–D plastic map of the Grand Canyon National Park.

● Officials in Arizona (and other states) are using the pictures to measure the snowcover in the state so as to measure more accurately the snowmelt run-off into reservoirs. This allows them a more scientific basis for deciding whether or not to release water

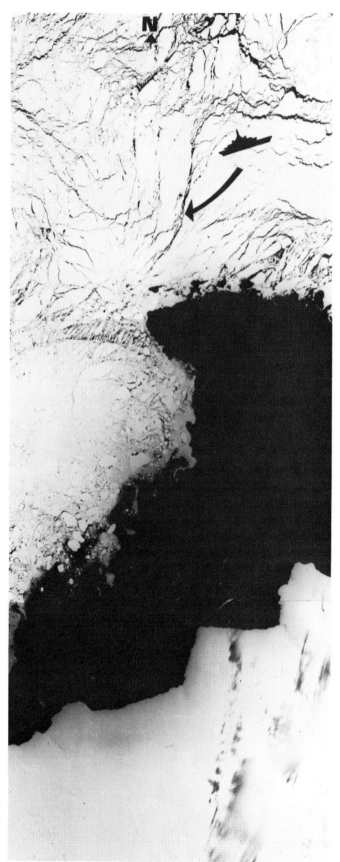

Landsat images of cracks in the ice
(see arrow) allowed research ship
to get to Pine Island Bay.

in reservoirs as the snow begins to melt. On the one hand, this can prevent flooding and damage to dams when too much water is running down from the mountains, and, on the other hand, it prevents the unnecessary waste of fresh water by spilling off more reservoir water than is required by the situation. An official of the Geological Survey has said that this one type of Landsat application alone has "the potential of saving users many millions of dollars."

● One of the most remarkable systems that has been developed in conjunction with Landsat is one in which a computer and a set of images work together to crank out a crop map of an entire region in a matter of hours. The resulting map shows the exact location and size of each crop, with C for corn, S for soybean, W for wheat, and so forth and with each letter representing an acre of land. Such maps look like this:

```
CCCCCCCCCCCCWWWWWWWWWWSSSSSSSSS
CCCCCCCCWWWWWWWWWWWWWSSSSSSSSSS
CCCCCCCCWWWWWWWWWWWWWWWSSSSSSSSS
CCCCCCCCWWWWWWWWWWWWWWWWSSSSSSSSSS
CCCCCCCCWWWWWWWWWWWWWWWWSSSSSSSSSS
CCCCCCCCWWWWWWWWWWWWWWWWWWWWW
```

Similar maps have been produced that accurately distinguish between stands of hardwood and pine.

● The American Automobile Association is using Landsat pictures to create mountain relief road maps. They have already published such maps for Alaska, Idaho/Montana, Arizona/New Mexico, and northern New England with the help of 1,900 frames of Landsat images, and are now working on maps of Germany, Austria, Italy, Switzerland, Scandinavia, and the Balkans.

● An Israeli Landsat investigator has come up with findings that may explain a major cause of deserts and droughts in the Middle East. He has found that the soils of the Sinai, denuded of vegetation by the grazing of goats and sheep, are cooler than those in the neighboring Negev where grazing is controlled and where there is significant plant life. Because of this, the Negev absorbs more heat from the sun, which then heats the air. This heated air creates a "heat mountain" which rises to form clouds and rain. The Sinai, which has no such heat mountain, has much less rain. "As a gross oversimplification," he explains, "it can be postulated that a population explosion in grazing herds during the 'seven fat years' is the cause of the 'seven lean years.' " One Landsat photo of the area shows a distinct line between the two deserts; it not only shows the contrast in grazing policy, but also coincides with the 1948–1949 Israeli–Egyptian Armistice Line.

● The South Dakota State University Remote Sensing Institute has combined pictures of that state with other information to create maps that classify soil types. A set of images that cost $80.00 were used to create one county soil map which would have cost

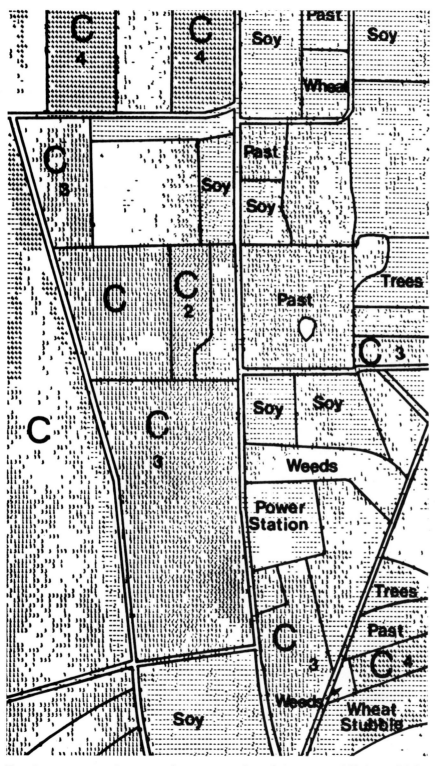

Earth resources photography was used to detect corn blight, which is then notated by computer printout. C2 areas have very mild blight, C3 mild, and C4 moderately severe.

$14,000 if conventional aerial photographs had been used. Aside from the obvious land-use planning feature of this work, part of the significance of these maps is that South Dakota assesses land taxes on the potential productivity of farm land rather than its sale value.

● Scientists working for the Geological Survey have discovered surface features not apparent on the ground or from aircraft which reveal faults believed to be associated with past earthquakes in the Mississippi Valley area—the center of a series of quakes in 1811–1812 that were the most severe in the known history of the United States and that were felt throughout an area of one million square miles. This discovery prompted two government geologists to conclude in a 1975 paper, "All the features described here suggest . . . that, apart from other evidence, major earthquakes may occur locally through time anywhere throughout this region."

● Experimenters have used electronically enhanced Landsat images to detect oil slicks in various parts of the world, ranging from the Gulf of Suez to offshore Santa Barbara. The promise of this finding lies in the ability to pinpoint the source of spills (Landsat showed, for example, that a 1975 Santa Barbara oil slick came from rock fissures rather than drilling platforms) as well as to detect spills and seeps not visible on earth in such places as along the Alaskan North Slope, where they can be obscured by snow or ice.

● A major national effort, the Landsat–Bolivia Project, has produced important results for that nation, including an improved national atlas, the discovery of previously uncharted lakes, and the routing of a major gas pipeline through the country, a feat that would have cost millions of dollars using conventional procedures for planning and surveying.

● In one dramatic demonstration, five previously unknown copper deposits were located in Pakistan and later verified on the ground. The Pakistani government is now examining the sites to see if the remote deposits are rich enough to exploit commercially. As in other examples of armchair prospecting, the clues to these deposits were not visible to the naked eye and were only revealed when the Landsat images were computer enhanced.

The list goes on and on. Safety officials in several states are learning where faults intersect with underground coal mines, enabling them to mark these areas of high cave-in potential for special precautions. Others are using the same kind of fault-revealing picture to decide where *not* to place nuclear power plants. Authorities in Tennessee are using pictures of the state to check on the recovery programs for land that has been strip mined. An oil pipeline in Canada's McKenzie Valley was rerouted to an area free of the fragile permafrost after this course was revealed by satellite image. Pictures of the area around oil-rich Prudhoe Bay in Alaska suggest the presence of even more oil than had been originally estimated.

Also, the pictures are beginning to be used to make general points about the earth that are not limited to a single geographic

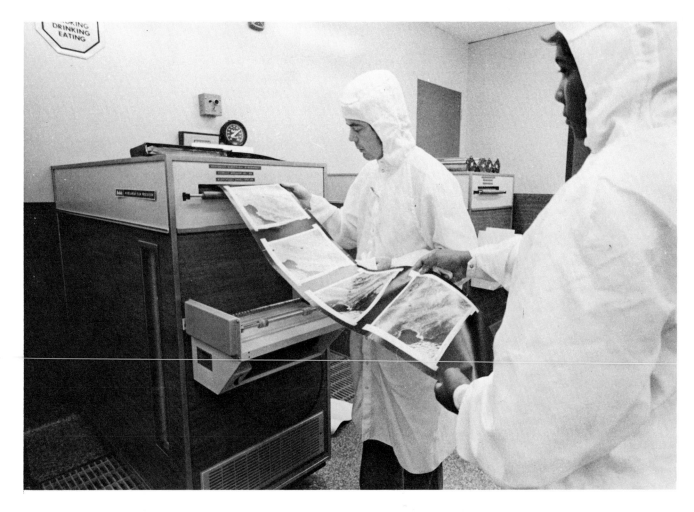

area. In one such example, scientists have used the data to come to the conclusion that man takes fresh water from only about one percent of the total supply available.

Landsat has already proven to be a major success and has exceeded the hopes of its most enthusiastic early supporters. Ironically, the Space Agency, which had to be pushed into the project in the first place, is now the proudest of fathers. Top NASA officials, such as Administrator Fletcher, seldom miss a chance to brag about it. On the occasion of the launch of the second satellite, he said, "If I had to pick one spacecraft, one Space Age development to save the world, I would pick ERTS and the satellites which I believe will be evolved from it later in the decade." More recently he remarked that he believed the economic benefits of these satellites to the United States will prove to be enough to totally offset the cost of the *entire* space program.

Meanwhile, there is an important postscript to this story which indicates that the civilian Landsat effort is less exact than present technology allows. This is the side of the business of satellite imagery from space that cannot be overlooked, but often is. Without

Landsat images being processed at NASA's Goddard Space Flight Center.

question the most sophisticated, detailed, and revealing photographs of the earth taken from orbit are never seen by the public nor, for that matter, by the scientific community. These are the images produced by military spy satellites that are wrapped in such secrecy that *even the name* of the government organization in charge, the National Reconnaissance Office, was classified "top secret" until it inadvertently appeared in a Senate report in 1973. The NRO is run by a group of specialists with some of the highest level security clearances in all government. It serves a limited list of clients which include the CIA, the Defense Intelligence Agency, and the White House. These satellites, which carry names like Samos and "Big Bird," have cost billions of dollars to develop and fly. On the average, in recent years the US has put up seven to eight a year while the Soviet Union launches thirty annually.

Publicly at least, civilian scientists seldom talk about the military side of space imaging, but when they do it is most revealing. One space scientist told a *Fortune* magazine writer in 1968, "When we [NASA] imply by the use of the Gemini photographs that the best we can fly in space is a Hasselblad, we are committing a patent lie." More recently, an obscure federal task force looking at advanced mapping techniques put a line in its final report that reveals some of the frustration that civilian scientists and technicians feel about the images they can never see. In an obvious reference to Landsat, the task force expressed its displeasure with "expensive systems for civilian use that cannot compete in any meaningful way with Department of Defense-developed technology."

The resolution of these images is spectacular if one is to believe the testimony of those who have seen them. Several years ago, the Pentagon itself said its satellite images were so detailed that a small car could be seen on the ground. Other sources, however, say that this understates the true ability of these spy satellites which can resolve down to one foot from orbit, which would mean that Soviet chickens could be counted from space. If this sounds incredible, it is a small accomplishment when compared with what has been planned for the military's Survsatcoms (Survivable Satellite Communications Satellites), which will go into operation in the 1980s. One function of these satellites will be to transmit *live* television pictures of the highest resolution from almost any part of the world. It will allow, among other things, the President and the top military brass to watch a crisis unfold halfway around the world.

6

Mars Illustrated

As was made so graphic in the case of the moon, photography not only showed us where we ultimately *got to*, but also showed us where we *could go* thanks to the automated spacecraft that did all the early reconnaissance.

If and when a decision is made to send humans to Mars, history will repeat itself since all of preliminary homework will have been done by unmanned photographic agents. Already probes, orbiters, and landers have taken increasingly clear images on and around Mars and sent them back a distance of over 200 million miles. If there are to be no manned missions, our knowledge of the planet has already increased tremendously and will continue to increase as more sophisticated robots are sent to roam the Martian surface.

The first American images of Mars were gathered by Mariner probes winging by the planet, one in 1965 and two in 1969, which rendered crude images indicating Mars was dominated by a moon-like cratered surface. Then in 1971–1972 the Mariner 9 Orbiter transmitted 7,000 detailed pictures that showed a surprisingly diverse planet with giant volcanoes, layered terrain, and a valley extending a fifth of the way around its circumference.

However, the most stunning accomplishment occurred in the summer of 1976 when a pair of Viking spacecraft dispatched Volkswagen-sized landers to the surface of Mars. These landers performed what must be considered the most sophisticated acts of photographic virtuosity even when they began sending back images as good as, and in some cases better than, what a human standing in the same spot would have seen with the naked eye.

Each lander carried a pair of facsimile cameras that looks like a set of periscopes from the outside. Within seconds of the first lander's touchdown it took a picture that showed the footpad of the lander against the Martian soil. Then, later in the day, it began working on a panoramic view of its new surroundings encompassing some 300 degrees of the rocky, wind-swept terrain. The next day, it began working in color and completed a work showing that Mars looked like it had been doused with a red-rust stain. In the days that followed, there were more photos from both landers, including panoramas and smaller images switching from color to black and white, to infrared, and, with a pair of cameras, to stereographic pairs.

These cameras are highly sophisticated and versatile examples of the facsimile principle that has been in use for many years to scan wire service news photos for radio or telephone transmission. They each weigh sixteen pounds, and the four had taken Itek Optical Sys-

Martian images being received from Mariner 9.

tems almost five years to design and build to specifications that would allow them to record top quality images from a distant and unusual environment. Where film would be found in a conventional camera, these have tiny light-sensitive devices (photo-diodes) that pick up one minute picture element (pixel) at a time until one thin line of the image has been scanned. The entire camera is then moved slightly to get the next line, and this continues at the rate of about five lines a second until the whole picture is taken. This time-consuming one-line at a time process explains why each camera can take only a few pictures each day. To get all this back to earth, each pixel is converted into an electronic signal that is transmitted to earth at the speed of light. On the ground, the process is reversed as the signal is converted back to light which, in turn, is scanned over film to prepare a negative one line at a time. Before the pictures are finished, they are "enhanced" through a computer technique that extracts additional detail from the picture.

To a purist these astonishingly clear images are not true photographs in the traditional sense, but electronic images. Nor, for that matter, are the pictures from Landsat, the weather satellites, the unmanned lunar explorers, or the television still cameras on the two Viking orbiters, true photographs. Whatever you choose to call them, they are magnificent.

It will take a long time for all of these pictures to be studied in full, but a preliminary assessment of their importance was given by Viking Project Scientist Dr. Gerald Soffen in a November, 1976 press conference at the National Press Club in Washington. He began by discussing the television images from the Viking orbiters and then moved on to the lander cameras. Here is some of what he reported:

Let me just recall some of the high points that the orbiter cameras have taken. We have seen a planet of extreme heterogeneity. We have seen a planet that is obviously deeply affected by fluvial activity. A great deal of flow has taken place. The craters were far beyond our imaginations. We have seen erosion, we have seen deposition. . . . The polar regions are just beginning to get known, and as the season progresses we will see more of them. We have seen hazes, we have seen fogs. We have now seen sand dunes . . . [a]nd we have observed the satellites of Mars. . . . And we have confirmed that . . . in fact the pole is made of water. . . .

On the lander, I think, the pictures speak for themselves. . . . They really are dramatic enough. Many people have for the first time come to believe that Mars is indeed a red planet. We have been lucky enough to land in the two major geological formations, the rocky terrain with those fine particles. We have seen a variety of rocks running all the way from very smooth, fine-grained rocks to the vesicular rocks that have holes that suggest gas bubbles. And, in fact, for the first time we have begun to understand something about the geological processes.

There was another participant in that news conference who talked about some of the things the landers did *not* see. Without getting into the larger question of life being found on Mars, it is worthwhile to hear what one of the leading experts in the field of extraterrestrial biology, who is also a member of the NASA Lander Imaging Team, has to say about the possibility that the cameras missed something. These were some of the comments made by Dr. Carl Sagan of Cornell University:

Now, the question of the imaging experiment. If there were large forms of life, forms big enough to see on Mars, the two cameras on each of the two landers had a fair chance of seeing them, at least in the times and places of the landing sites. We have photographed details smaller than a millimeter across. We have the ability to detect moving objects. . . . And these results are entirely negative.

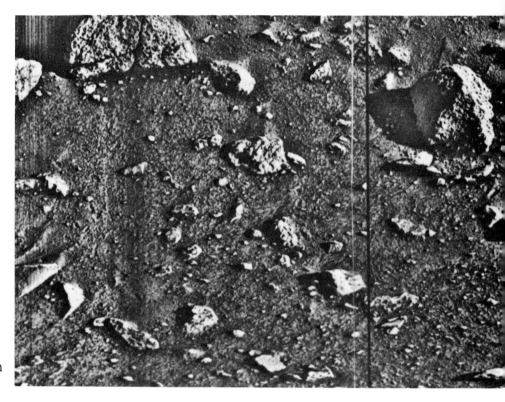

The first photograph ever taken from the surface of Mars.

There are no bushes, trees, cacti, giraffes, antelopes, rabbits. There are no burrows, tracks, footprints, spoor. There are no patches of color which are uniquely attributable to photosynthetic pigments. In short, there is not the faintest hint on a scale large enough to see at these two places, at these two times, of anything live.

Now, having said that, let me make a few caveats. One is that we have examined one ten-millionth of the surface of Mars with the two landings, and it might well be that they are not characteristic of the other places on the planet.

For example, if I were to drop you into two random places on the planet Earth, these would very likely be oceans, and you would not see any large forms of life in short periods of time, and you would simply disappear from view. In addition, there are many places on the land area of Earth, like the great Peruvian desert, where as far as the eye can see there is nothing alive whatsoever; and, yet, in the oceans and the Peruvian desert, those places are loaded with microorganisms.

So the absence of large organisms, while certainly relevant to the question of life on the planet, by no means can be considered to exclude the presence of smaller organisms—microbes. . . .

The two places which were chosen for Viking landing are two of the dullest places on the planet we could find. We chose them purposely for their dullness, because dullness and safety go hand in hand, and, certainly, the primary objective of the mission was to get it down safely, and do science. We should not, therefore,

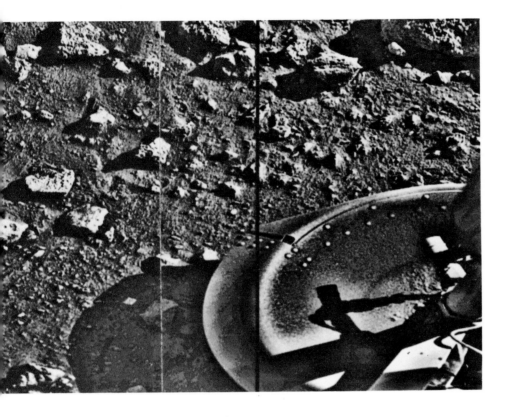

conclude that there aren't much more exciting places for biology, geology and everything else on the planet.

Finally, on imaging, let me note that for the great fraction of this history of our planet you could have landed on any place on the surface of the Earth and seen a terrain probably not much different from the typical views of Mars taken from the Viking landers. Nothing large to see, and yet a wide variety of microorganisms in the soil, because organisms large enough to see have arisen in the Earth only during the last billion years, and life has been on the planet something like 4 billion years.

These remarks become even more intriguing when one realizes that Sagan, along with other scientists working on the Viking data, has by no means excluded the possibility of finding microorganisms in some other location, or under other conditions that were not examined by the Vikings.

While human attention naturally tends to focus on Mars, which is the planet most like Earth, it is important not to lose sight of the Pioneer and Mariner spacecraft, to say nothing of their Soviet counterparts, which have already sent back thousands of images from Mercury, Venus, Jupiter, and Saturn. These photographs have not only shown that good images can be made from much further out than Mars, but that these tough little robots, replete with cameras and scientific instruments, can fetch pictures of inhospitable realms that, at this point in time, humans cannot hope to approach.

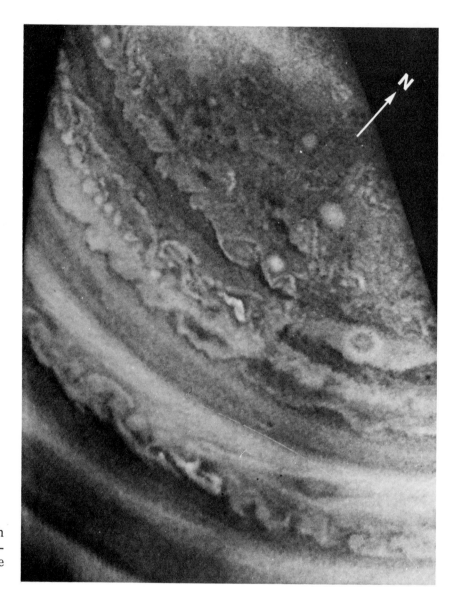

Pioneer 11 picture of Jupiter which shows for the first time what appears to be gigantic storms in the planet's north polar region.

Consider, for example, the pictures of Jupiter which Pioneer Jupiter spacecraft have sent back to us. Jupiter, the largest planet in our solar system, appears as an almost entirely liquid planet without any solid surface, with winds as high as 360 miles per hour. It has inner radiation belts with intensities comparable to those found in nuclear explosions, and its Great Red Spot, long a mystery, now appears to be the center of a gigantic storm that has been raging for hundreds of years along a 25,000-mile front.

7

UFOs and Allegedly Suppressed Photographs

A number of stories are circulating which claim that NASA and/or NOAA possess secret photo files that the public cannot see. The stories fall into two classes: those which claim that the censored images have been intercepted for reasons of military security because they reveal a secret installation or tell too much about missile placement and, second, those which show UFOs, evidence of a lunar or Martian civilization, or prove that visitors from another planet have been on earth. There may be some truth to the first claim, since it is no secret that the military has reviewed some NASA flight films, although a source involved in the initial screening of film at NASA says he is unaware of any being pulled by the military.

As for UFOs and evidence of extraterrestrial life, there is no evidence to suggest a cover-up. Such a conspiracy would have required the collusion of the governments of the US and the USSR, astronauts and cosmonauts, and a large number of individual scientists, technicians, and policymakers. After talking with many of those involved with space photography, I have become convinced that NASA would not only release these pictures if they had them, but that they would be the first to exploit them. There is strong motivation at NASA to find evidence of life elsewhere in the universe, because such a discovery would give the agency credit for what would have to be the greatest scientific discovery in human history. Among other things, such a finding would spawn a program of further investigation that would give NASA a budget that would dwarf the funds spent on the Apollo program. The fact that NASA wants to find extraterrestrial life was underscored by the real disappointment at not finding life on Mars with the Viking landers. Periodically, NASA makes new attempts to communicate with other beings, as it did in 1972 by attaching a gold pictorial plaque to the Pioneer F spacecraft which is on its way to becoming the first man-made object to enter interstellar space. NASA's stated purpose for the plaque was, "to show scientifically educated inhabitants of some other star system—who might intercept it millions of years from now—when Pioneer was launched, from where, and by what kind of beings."

Even if one believed that the official space establishment would hide such evidence, it is all but impossible to believe that one or more of the individuals involved would not opt for fame and a gargantuan publisher's advance to go public with the story. Or, as one NASA scientist put it, "I know of no scientists who could be trusted to sit on a discovery that would immortalize their names."

There are also several stories that have given special otherworldly or conspiratorial interpretations to photographs which are already public. One outlandish example which refuses to be stilled began some years ago when *Science* magazine published a view of the Southern Hemisphere which was a mosaic of individual photographs taken by a weather satellite in polar orbit. There was a large black circle at the center of the picture where the South Pole is located. The hole or black spot occurred because this area was not photographed by the satellite. However, for a number of those who subscribe to the theory that UFOs are actually the property of the US Air Force, the hole in the mosaic became the secret opening in the earth where these vehicles were based. NOAA has a thick file of letters relating to this picture and the many other holes-in-the-pole mosaics it has produced over the years. If, indeed, there was a hole of the size shown in these pictures, it would have to be thousands of square miles in size and would have required the most extensive excavation in human history. Others have accused NOAA of suppressing photos which they claim show important new information on the Bermuda Triangle. This is an especially hard allegation to swallow, as there are now more than 500 stations around the world which automatically receive these images, including scientists and radio amateurs with no government ties. To suppress such images would require an impossible secret conspiracy involving thousands of individuals and scores of governments.

Of all the duly released pictures that have come out of the space program, however, none has matched the stir created by those taken by Scott Carpenter of a balloon experiment performed on the seventh Mercury flight. One of the jobs Carpenter was assigned to perform in orbit was to inflate and deploy a special multicolored balloon which was to be attached to the capsule by a 100-foot nylon braided line. The purpose of this exercise was twofold: to observe the balloon's colors to see how they showed up in space, and to get drag measurements on the balloon and its line. Carpenter got the balloon out, observed it, and took pictures of it, but the experiment was not altogether successful as the balloon failed to inflate properly, giving it a flat, saucer-like shape. Those pictures have been used repeatedly to support the claim that Carpenter's capsule was followed by classic saucer-shaped UFOs. In fact, recently, one of these pictures was actually mislabeled as a Skylab photograph and published in a magazine to support the contention that Skylab had company too. Even though Carpenter's balloon experiment was publicly announced before launch, those who believe in a conspiracy to cover-up UFO data think that NASA fabricated the balloon story.

There seems to be no end to the claims that NASA is hiding or misinterpreting important material. When I talked with NASA photographic expert Dick Underwood in late 1976, he reported that the first allegations were starting to reach his office in Houston to the effect that pictures from the Viking landers which showed life on Mars were being suppressed by the same people whose job it was to search for evidence of life there. In fact, Underwood's morning mail had contained a letter demanding the immediate release of the pictures that showed Martians attacking the landers.

Unquestionably, NASA would love to comply.

8

How to Obtain Your Own Space Photographs

LANDSAT IMAGES

Earth images taken by Landsats 1 and 2 can be purchased by the public in a variety of formats and sizes. Here is a listing of the major sources:

User Services Unit
EROS Data Center
Sioux Falls, South Dakota 57198
Phone: (605) 594–6511

False color composites, black and white images, film positives and negatives, and copies of 16 mm microfilm for reviewing large numbers of images are all available for sale from this group. Write or call for current prices and a catalog. Also, requests for information about pictures of a specific geographic area will initiate a free computerized search.

National Climatic Center
Satellite Data Services Branch
World Weather Building
Room 606, D543
5200 Auth Road
Washington, D.C. 20233
Phone: (301) 763–8111

Much of the same material that is available from the EROS Center can be obtained from the following group which also issues free information and price lists:

General Electric Space Division
5030 Herzel Place
Beltsville, Maryland 20705
Phone: (301) 345–9344

Slide sets, prints, mosaics, and transparencies can be obtained from the GE Photo Lab. Write for a listing of images available.

Cartographic Division

Soil Conservation Service
Federal Center, Building No. 1
Hyattsville, Maryland 20782
Phone: (301) 436–8182

This source has black and white mosaics of the coterminous US and Alaska.

National Cartographic Information Center
US Geological Survey
507 National Center
Reston, Virginia 22092
Phone: (703) 860–6045

This is an information center which, among other things, has browsing files for Landsat images and supplies information on what images are available. It also sells images in various sizes and formats.

U.S. Geological Survey
Branch of Distribution
1200 South Eads Street
Arlington, Virginia 22202

The following special lithographic items can be purchased from this source:

• A copy of the mosaic of the US, scale 1: 5,000,000, price $1.25.

• Mosaic of Arizona in black and white or sepia with cultural and drainage information overprinted, size 48 by 60 inches, scale 1:5,000,000, price $1.25 for black and white, $1.25 for sepia.

• State of Florida mosaic in "false color," size 44 by 58 inches, scale 1:500,000, $3.00 a copy.

• New Jersey in "false color," scale 1:500,000, $1.25 per copy.

• The Upper Chesapeake Bay in "false color," scale 1:500,000, price $1.25.

Bara Photographic, Inc.
4805 Frolich Lane
Hyattsville, Maryland 20781
Phone: (301) 322–7900

This is a private source of Landsat slides, prints, and transparencies. Write or call for prices and information.

"HOME TOWN" PHOTOS FROM SPACE

Because of the demand for them, the Geological Survey has simplified procedures for obtaining color pictures of 103 cities and metropolitan areas which have been taken by Landsat, Skylab, and NASA high altitude aircraft. Pictures are offered for the following areas coded with an A (aircraft), S (Skylab), or L (Landsat) to show the coverage available. If you are offered a choice of more than one type of coverage for the city you are interested in, this should help you make your selection:

Landsat—Widest area of coverage of the three. Rivers, large airports, some highways—but not individual homes and streets—can be seen.

Skylab—Taken from an altitude of 270 miles, these clearly reveal roads, streets, shopping centers, and other large buildings, such as schools and apartment houses, but not individual houses.

Aircraft—Shows individual homes, but not cars and trucks.

Albany, NY	A,L	Cincinnati, OH	A,L
Albuquerque, NM	A,L	Cleveland, OH	A,S,L
Akron, OH	A,S,L	Columbus, OH	A,L
Anaheim, CA	A,L	Dallas, TX	A,L
Atlanta, GA	A,L	Davenport, IA	A,L
Baltimore, MD	A,S,L	Dayton, OH	L
Baton Rouge, LA	A,S,L	Denver, CO	A,L
Beaumont, TX	A,L	Detroit, MI	A,S,L
Bethlehem/		El Paso, TX	A,S,L
Allentown, PA	A,S,L	Flint, MI	A,S,L
Birmingham, AL	A,S,L	Fresno, CA	A,S,L
Boston, MA	A,S,L	Ft. Lauderdale, FL	A,L
Bridgeport, CT	A,S,L	Ft. Wayne, IN	L
Buffalo, NY	A,L	Ft. Worth, TX	A,L
Canton, OH	A,L	Gary, IN	A,S,L
Charleston, SC	A,L	Grand Rapids, MI	A,S,L
Charlotte, NC	L	Greensboro, NC	A,L
Chattanooga, TN	A,L	Greenville, SC	L
Chicago, IL	A,S,L	Harrisburg, PA	A,S,L

Hartford, CT	A,S,L	Peoria, IL	A,S,L
Honolulu, HI	A	Philadelphia, PA	A,L
Houston, TX	A,L	Phoenix, AZ	A,S,L
Indianapolis, IN	A,L	Pittsburgh, PA	A,S,L
Jacksonville, FL	A,L	Portland, OR	A,L
Jersey City, NJ	A,S,L	Providence, RI	A,L
Kansas City, KS/		Raleigh/Durham,	
MO	A,L	NC	A,L
Knoxville, TN	A,S,L	Richmond, VA	A,L
Lansing, MI	A,S,L	Rochester, NY	A,L
Long Branch, NJ	A,L	Sacramento, CA	A,L
Los Angeles, CA	A,L	Salt Lake City, UT	A,S,L
Louisville, KY	A,S,L	San Antonio, TX	L
Memphis, TN	A,L	San Bernadino, CA	A,L
Miami, FL	A,L	San Diego, CA	A,S,L
Milwaukee, WI	A,L	San Francisco, CA	A,S,L
Minneapolis/St.		San Jose, CA	A,S,L
Paul, MN	A,S,L	Seattle, WA	A,L
Mobile, AL	A,S,L	Shreveport, LA	A,L
Nashville, TN	S,L	Sioux Falls, SD	A,S,L
Nassau/Suffolk,		Springfield, MA	A,S,L
NY	A,L	St. Louis, MO	A,S,L
New Brunswick, NJ	A,S,L	St. Petersburg, FL	A,L
New Haven, CT	A,S,L	Syracuse, NY	A,S,L
New Orleans, LA	A,L	Tacoma, WA	A,L
New York, NY	A,S,L	Tampa, FL	A,L
Newark, NJ	A,S,L	Toledo, OH	A,L
Norfolk, VA	A,L	Tucson, AZ	A,L
Northeast		Utica/Rome, NY	A,L
(Scranton), PA	A,L	Washington, DC	A,S,L
Oklahoma City, OK	A,L	West Palm Beach,	
Omaha, NE	S,L	FL	A,L
Orlando, FL	A,L	Wichita, KS	L
Oxnard/Simi Valley,		Wilmington, DE	A,L
CA	A,L	Worcester, MA	A,S,L
Patterson, NJ	A,S,L	Youngstown, OH	S,L

The present prices for "false color" Landsat images are $7.00 for a 7 by 7-inch print, $20.00 for a 15 by 15-inch print, and $40.00 for a 30 by 30-inch print. Natural color Skylab pictures are $7.00 for 5 by 5- or 9 by 9-inch prints, $20.00 for 17 by 17-inch prints, and $40.00 for 34 by 34-inch prints. Color aerial photos run $7.00 for a 9 by 9-inch print, $20.00 for an 18 by 18-inch print, $25.00 for a 27 by 27-inch print, and $40.00 for a 36 by 36-inch print. Order forms are available from the User Services Unit, Eros Data Center, Sioux Falls, South Dakota 57198. Orders can also be sent in letter form if exact details are included (i.e., city, type of coverage, and size of image.)

METEOROLOGICAL IMAGES
The key address in this area is:

Satellite Data Services Branch
World Weather Building
Room 606
Washington, D.C. 20233
Phone: (301) 763–8111

Files at the Satellite Data Services Branch contain images beginning with those taken by the first TIROS satellites through the most recent taken by the weather satellites now in operation. It also has major holdings of Landsat and Skylab images. Visitors are welcome at the Washington facility where "browse files" have been established to improve public access to the images. There are additional browse files located at thirty-nine other locations throughout the country, and a current list of their addresses and phone numbers can be obtained free of charge by writing to the main address provided above.

The costs of these images vary, depending on size and format; however, the most common types ordered are black and white prints in a standard 10 by 10-inch size that currently cost $2.50 apiece.

The people who work for Satellite Data Services are particularly helpful when dealing with the public and are quick to offer the catalogs, price lists, and order forms you will need to obtain the pictures you want.

NASA PHOTOGRAPHS
NASA photographs must be ordered through the agency's photographic contractor whose address is:

Space Photographs
P.O. Box 486
Bladensburg, Maryland 20710
Phone: (301) 322–7900

In order to do so, however, you must have the NASA headquarters photo numbers for the pictures you want (these are code numbers that include the letter H for black and white and H-C for color.) NASA will assist you free of charge in locating the picture numbers you want by writing or visiting:

National Aeronautics and Space Administration

Room 6035
400 Maryland Avenue, SW
Washington, D.C. 20546
Phone: (202) 755–8366

This office has become a mecca for space and photography buffs, who go there to review the tens of thousands of photographs on file. The collection represents what NASA believes to be the best and most important pictures taken as part of the total space program and includes both images taken on the ground and in space. It also contains hundreds of pictures of historic importance dating back as far as Goddard's early rocket experiments. While this office exists primarily to serve the news media and the pictorial needs of the rest of NASA, the staff always finds time to help the average citizen who drops in or writes. Despite an occasional rumor to the contrary, it does not give away photos free of charge to people outside the news media.

In order to give you an idea of their cost, here is a sampling of current prices:

Size	Single	Same subject/ 2 or more
Black and White Prints		
8 by 10	$1.75	$1.25
11 by 14	3.50	2.00
16 by 20	5.50	3.50
Color Prints		
8 by 10	5.00	3.50
11 by 14	9.00	6.00
16 by 20	18.00	12.00
Color Slides		
35 mm (cardboard mounted)	1.50	1.00
35 mm (glass mounted)	2.25	1.50
2¼ by 2¼ (cardboard)	2.00	1.25
Unmounted Color Transparencies		
4 by 5	5.00 each	
8 by 10	8.00 each	
11 by 14	12.00 each	

Other formats of the pictures can be ordered, including both black and white and color negatives and black and white slides. Write to either the NASA or contractor address for a full list of prices and detailed ordering instructions.

For those with a special interest in earth-oriented photographs from Gemini, Apollo, and Skylab missions, the following unit will send you information on the individual prints and slides it sells along with annotated educational slide sets:

Technology Application Center
University of New Mexico
Code 10
Albuquerque, New Mexico 87131

This group's color slide sets are of particular interest and include such titles as "Mainland China from Skylab, Apollo, Gemini" (31 slides, $27.90), "World Cities" (22 slides, $19.80), "Europe" (22 slides, $39.60), and "Full and Partial Earth Photos" (10 slides, $9.00).

First American Space Walk. One of James A. McDivitt's spectacular photographs of Edward H. White II during his 21-minute excursion outside the Gemini 4 spacecraft.

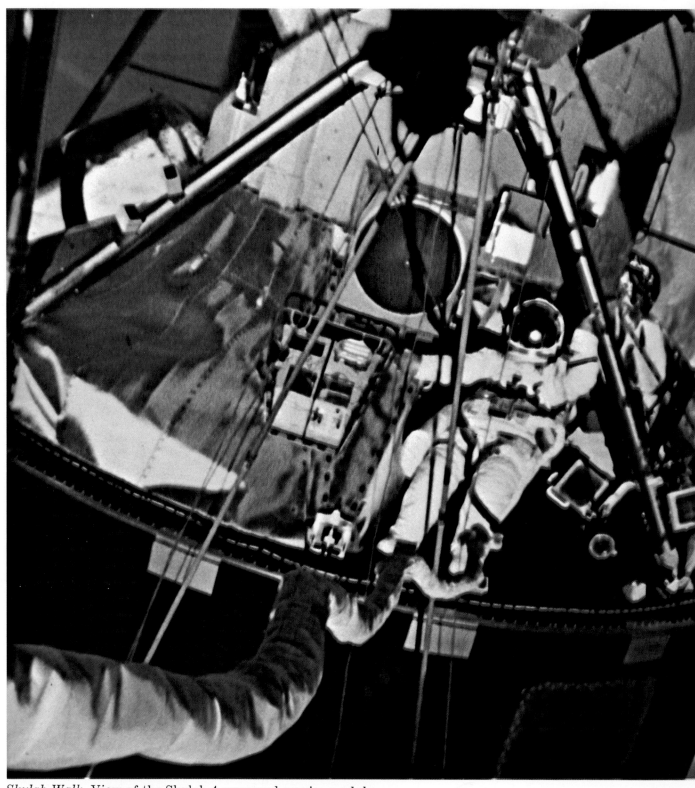

Skylab Walk. View of the Skylab 4 command service module showing scientist-astronaut Edward G. Gibson who has just come out of the hatchway.

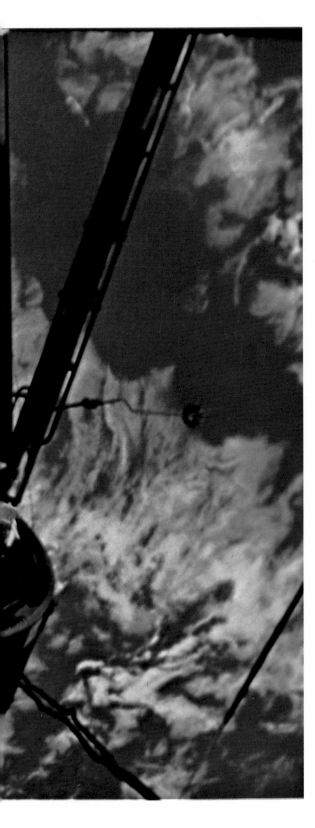

Adrift in Space. Another of McDivitt's sharp photographs of White. This series taken in 1965 is not only of historic importance, but it is also still widely regarded as the best sequence ever made of a man in space.

Portrait in Space. Walter M. Schirra, Apollo 7 commander, photographed during the mission.

"Angry Alligator." The Fiberglas shroud on this target vehicle failed to fall away when it was supposed to. This forced the cancellation of a docking maneuver with the Gemini 9 capsule but created some memorable images of an object that looks more like a powerfully jawed space monster than an inanimate piece of NASA hardware.

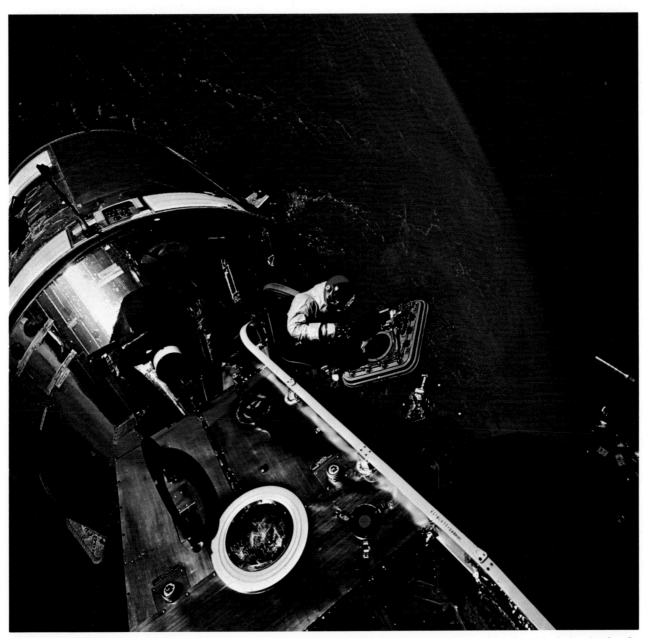

Man in a Hatch. The Apollo 9 command and lunar modules docked in orbit, with the earth in the background. David Scott stands in the open hatch of the command module in this picture taken by Russell Schweickart from the "porch" of the lunar module.

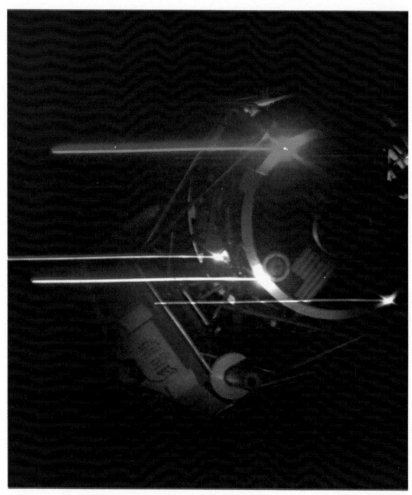

ABOVE: *Nighttime Separation.* Skylab 3 photograph taken from the command service module as the orbital workshop is let go in preparation for the return to earth. OPPOSITE: *Pinwheel Ahead.* View of the space station from the Skylab 4 command service module. The pinwheel section of the spacecraft is actually an array of solar panels used to gather energy. There is a rectangular solar panel on the rear of the vehicle. The one that is supposed to appear on the left was lost when the space station was launched for Skylab 2.

ABOVE: *Lunar Far Side*. This rich and deeply contrasted glimpse of the back of the moon was taken from the Apollo 15 command module. OPPOSITE: *Apollo Moon View*. Photograph of a nearly full moon taken from the Apollo 8 spacecraft.

ABOVE: *Aldrin on the Moon.* Undoubtedly the most famous of all space photographs. Apollo 11 astronaut Edwin E. Aldrin, Jr., standing awkwardly on the lunar surface with the lunar module and photographer Michael Collins reflected in his gold-plated visor. OPPOSITE: *"Intrepid."* The Apollo 12 lunar module, Intrepid, heading for its landing point on the Ocean of Storms. The large crater on the right, located approximately dead center on the near side of the moon, is Hershel.

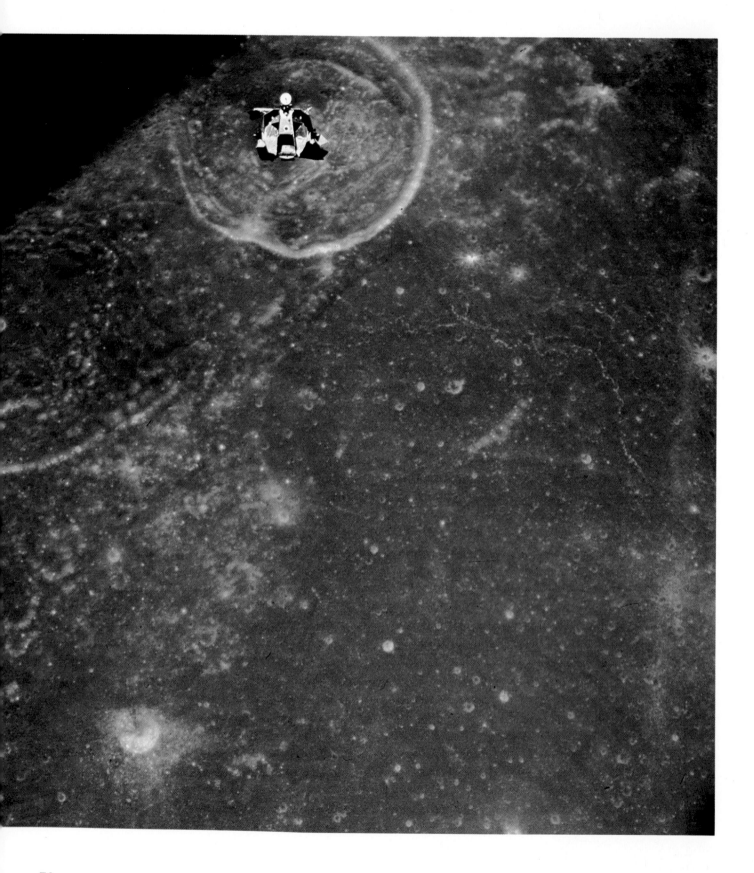

OPPOSITE: *Speck on Smith's Sea*. The Apollo 17 Lander is a small hunk of metal in this picture taken from lunar orbit. LEFT: *Earth, Flag, and Astronaut*. This picture of Harrison Schmitt posing next to the American flag is probably the most dramatic of all the "patriotic" moon photographs. Note that the American flag has been wired to "fly" on the windless moon. The blue marble at the tip of the flagpole is the earth. BELOW: *Moon Rock*. Astronaut Schmitt standing next to a mammoth split lunar boulder at the Apollo 17 Taurus-Littrow landing site.

ABOVE: *Half-lit Moon*. Photographed as Apollo 10 was passing high above the lunar equator. The Sea of Tranquility is the large dark area near the center. LEFT: *Classic Earth View*. The earth shines against the black backdrop of space in this Apollo 16 photograph. The United States and other parts of North America are visible. OPPOSITE: *Earthrise*. This sequence of three was taken from the Apollo 10 lunar module as it passed over the highlands on the far side of the moon.

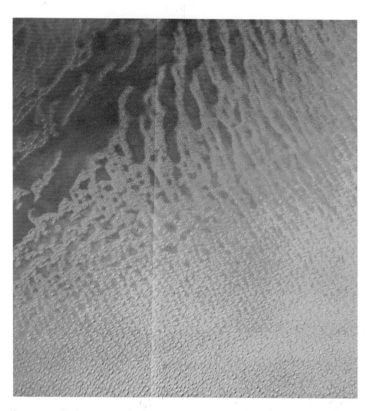

ABOVE: *Sahara Desert*. A nearly vertical view of an 8,000-square-mile portion of the Grand Erg Oriental of the Sahara from Skylab 3. It illustrates the variety of features that characterize the desert. The dark areas, for instance, are relatively sand free. OPPOSITE: *Northeast Africa and the Red Sea*. A particularly clear Gemini 11 photo taken from an altitude of approximately 470 nautical miles.

83

Forest Fires. An Apollo 7 image of northern Australia
that clearly shows the smoke plumes from a series of
major fires.

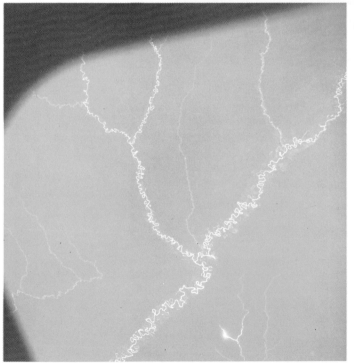

TOP: *Amazon Thunderclouds*. This image of storm clouds over the Amazon Basin, Brazil, was made on the Apollo 9 flight. BOTTOM LEFT: *Brazilian Rivers*. These tributaries of the Amazon show up with a clarity that turns this photograph from the Apollo-Soyuz mission into an instant map. BOTTOM RIGHT: *Typhoon Vortex*. Skylab 4 astronauts flew by this gigantic typhoon in the South Pacific, southeast of New Zealand.

ABOVE: *The Hindu Kush*. We can gaze into the deep chasms of the Himalayan Hindu Kush range in this Apollo 9 photograph. Clouds fill many of the valleys. OPPOSITE: *Bahama Island*. Berry Island of the Great Bahama Bank resembles a huge conch shell in this Skylab 4 picture.

15 APRIL

21 MAY

8 JUNE

6 AUGUST

Rocky Mountain Spring and Summer. Four Landsat images of the Wind River Range area of Wyoming. Pictures like these are invaluable to hydrologists, who use them to compute water runoff.

Cape Cod. This infrared color composite photo from Landsat 1 not only maps Cape Cod, Nantucket, and Martha's Vineyard, but also shows us how land is used. The red areas are the most heavily vegetated.

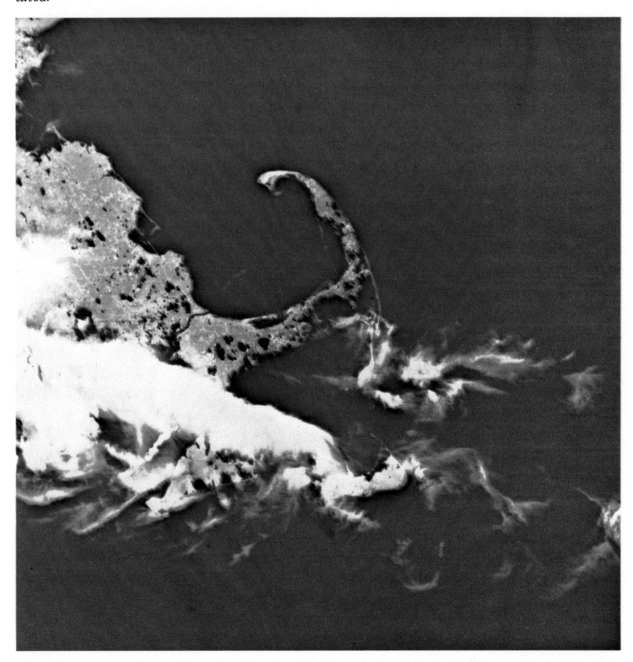

San Francisco. A dramatic display of an urban area painted in false color. For instance, the false color blue represents vegetation. This picture was taken at 50,000 feet by a NASA airplane experimenting with new earth-resources photographic techniques.

Nevada. East central Nevada from Skylab 2. The town of Ely is in the eastern corner of the picture, and the light area just west of town is a large copper mining pit. The alternating system of basins and ranges, which can be seen in this picture, is typical of this part of the country and has been described by geologists as looking like "worms migrating southward."

Southern Half of Florida. The Tampa Bay area, Lake Okeechobee, the Everglades, and the Florida Keys are all visible in this view from Gemini 12.

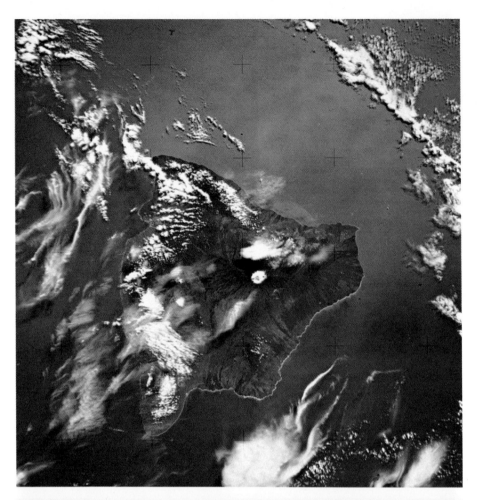

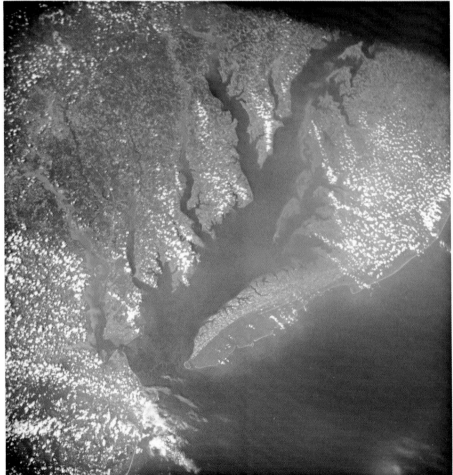

OPPOSITE TOP: *Hawaii*. The island of Hawaii against the blue of the Pacific. Snowcapped Mauna Loa and Mauna Kea appear in white in this Skylab 4 photograph. OPPOSITE BOTTOM: *Middle Atlantic*. Infrared picture taken from the Apollo spacecraft that docked with the Soviet Soyuz. It shows portions of Virginia, Delaware and Maryland, and the Chesapeake Bay. ABOVE: *Canadian Wilds*. This picture from the Apollo–Soyuz mission shows British Columbia, Alberta, and the Canadian Rockies. Snowcapped mountain peaks and glaciers are clearly visible in this July portrait. FOLLOWING PAGE: *Mars Exaggerated*. Viking image that has been processed by computer to draw out subtle color differences on the planet. Clouds, haze, surface frost, and bright deserts show up in shades of turquoise, white, and yellow. The giant Martian volcanoes are painted dark red against the yellow-orange of the plains which surround and fill their floors.

RIGHT: *Martian Hemisphere*. Color picture of Mars made from three images taken by the Viking 1 Orbiter on June 18, 1976. FAR RIGHT: *Mars in 3-D*. These are two pictures taken by Viking 1 cameras that were made to obtain a stereoscopic, or 3-D, view of the planet. The stereo effect can be seen by looking at the picture with any standard pocket stereo viewer.

LEFT: *Red Planet*. A two-hundred-degree sweep of the Martian horizon is shown in this composite of three color photos taken by Viking 2. The color of the planet is indeed rusty red, a condition caused by hydrated iron oxide. The dark red rocks on the right and left are volcanic. ABOVE: *Deep Hole*. Panoramic shot of the Viking 1 landing area taken in February, 1977 showing a 12-inch trench dug in the Martian surface (to the lower right of the boom) to obtain samples. Some red dust that has settled on the spacecraft can be seen in this picture.

Flag on Mars. Patriotism aside, this Viking image of a portion of the lander shows the familiar colors of the flag and Bicentennial logo underscoring the trueness of Viking color images of the red Martian landscape.

Jupiter's North. This Pioneer 10 picture shows a northern section of Jupiter that is not visible from the earth. Scientists have expressed the belief that the image shows an area of hurricane-like storms.

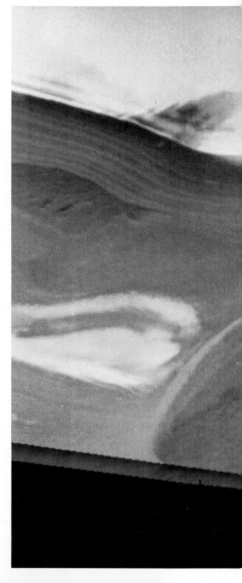

RIGHT: *Martian North Pole*. Three Viking Orbiter 2 images were combined to create this composite picture of Mars' North Pole, which shows both layered terrain and water ice. BELOW: *Deimos*. The smallest of Mars' two moons from a composite of two Viking Orbiter 1 images.

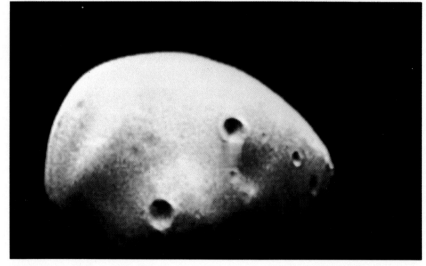

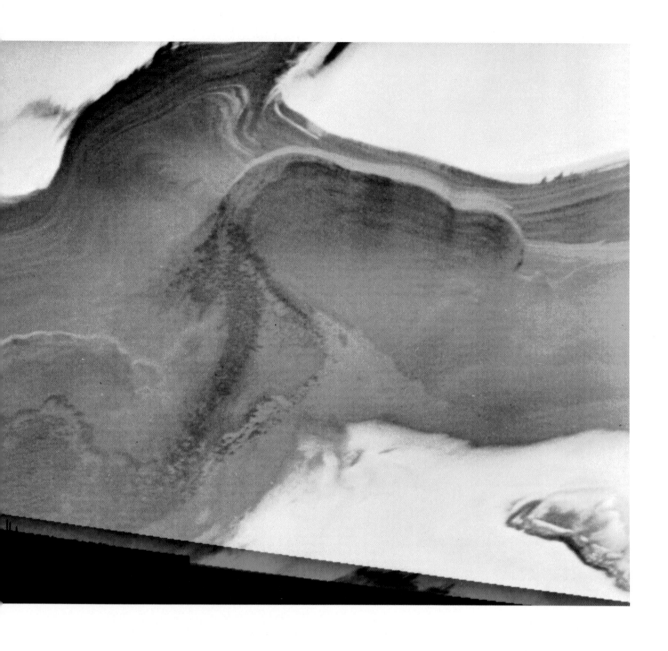

Sunset on Mars. Two versions of the same Viking 1 image of the Martian sunset over Chryse Planitia. The first is natural, and the second has been computer enhanced.

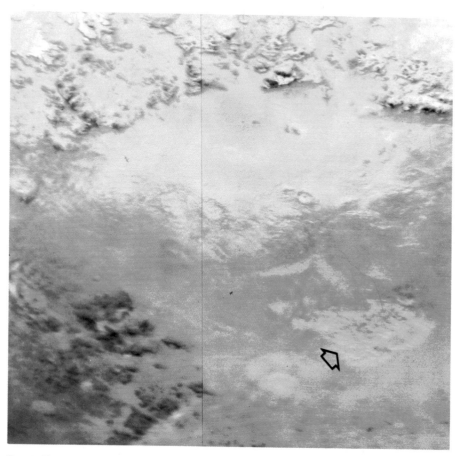

Dust Storm. The arrow which has been superimposed on this Viking Orbiter 2 photograph points to a turbulent dust storm some 186 miles wide.

Saturn. A NASA image made in 1968 with the help of the Catalina Observatory 61-inch telescope.

ABOVE: *Jupiter with Red Spot*. The planet's Great Red Spot shows up clearly in this Pioneer 11 picture. The dot in the center of the image is the shadow of the moon, Io. RIGHT: *Red Spot Close-up*. Pioneer 11 photo taken from a distance of 338,000 miles is the closest, most detailed image made to date of Jupiter's Great Red Spot. Scientists now believe that the Spot is actually a monstrous storm that has been raging along a 25,000-mile front for centuries.

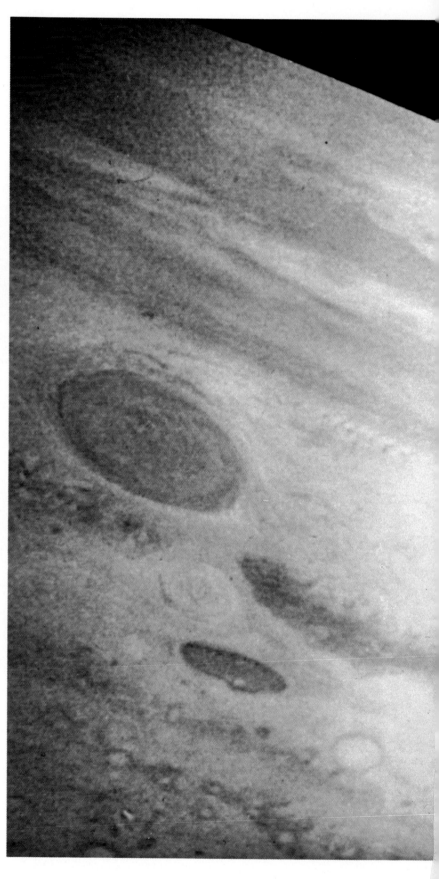

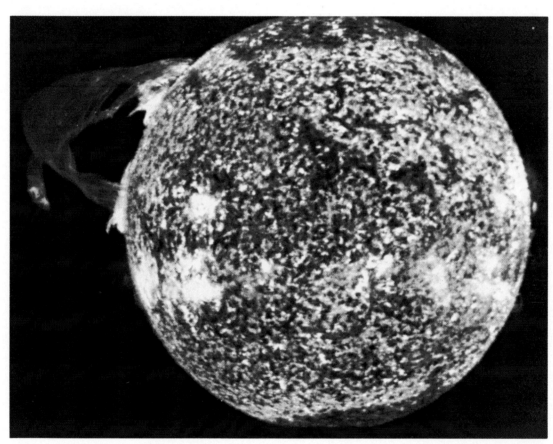

Giant Flare. One of the most spectacular solar flares ever sighted appears in the upper left of this Skylab 4 photograph. The base of the flare spreads across 367,000 miles of the solar surface.

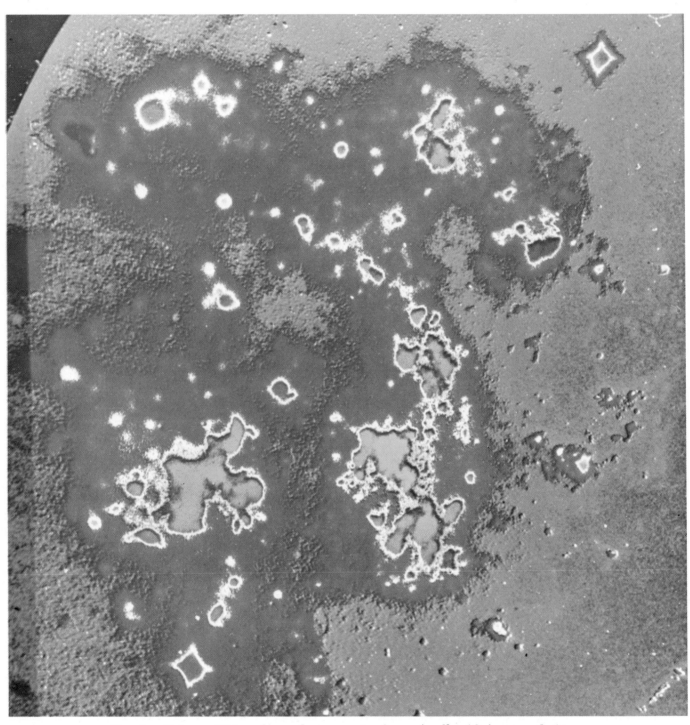

Nearby Galaxy. This color enhancement of an Apollo 16 image photographed in far-ultraviolet light shows a neighboring galaxy visible only from the earth's southern latitudes. The galaxy shown is a "young" one consisting of some 100 billion stars.

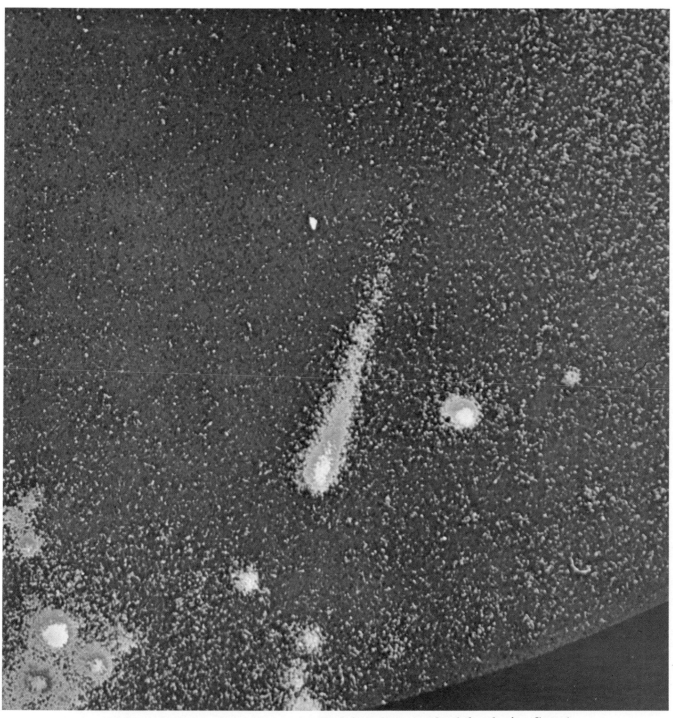

Kohoutek. This enhancement of a Skylab 4 photograph of the elusive Comet Kohoutek shows its relative levels of brightness. The comet's tail is three million miles long.

ABOVE: *Earth-like Terrain*. The Nilosyrtis region of Mars from the Viking Orbiter 1. The picture suggests geologic flow, perhaps aided by the process of freeze and thaw, like that found on earth. OPPOSITE: *Crater Yuty*. This crater appears to have been created by the collision of a meteorite with the surface of Mars. A portion of the Crater Wabash is visible on the right side of this Viking image.

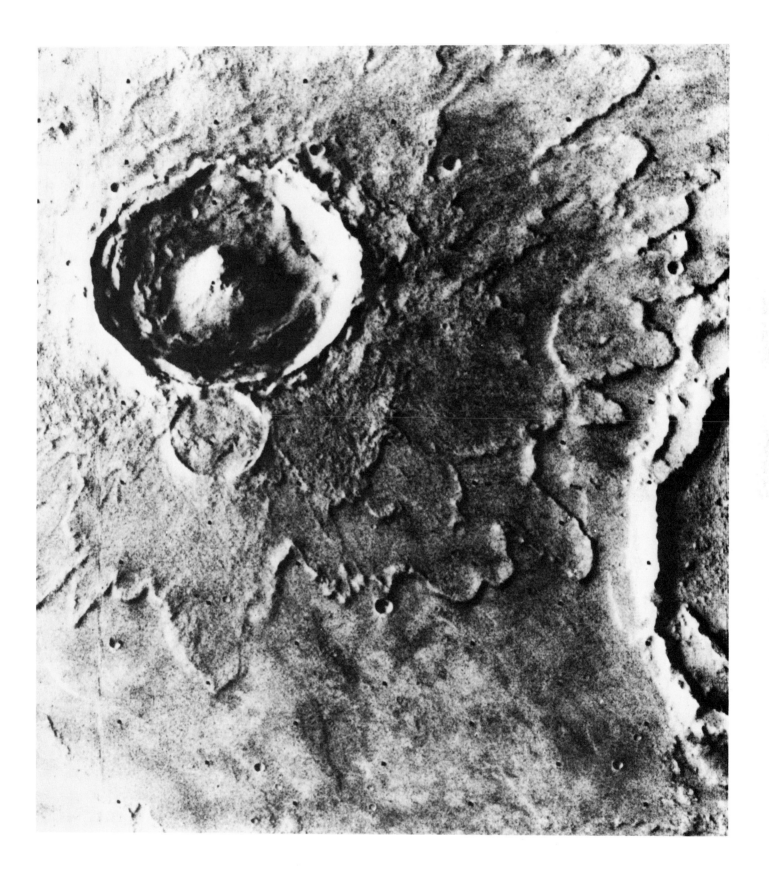

TOP: *Panorama.* This early morning view of the area around the Viking 1 Lander shows a field of sand dunes remarkably similar to those found on the deserts of earth, especially those in Mexico and California.

BOTTOM: *Rocky Plain.* The rocky terrain around the Viking 21 Lander is very detailed in this panorama shot taken during a September afternoon on Mars.

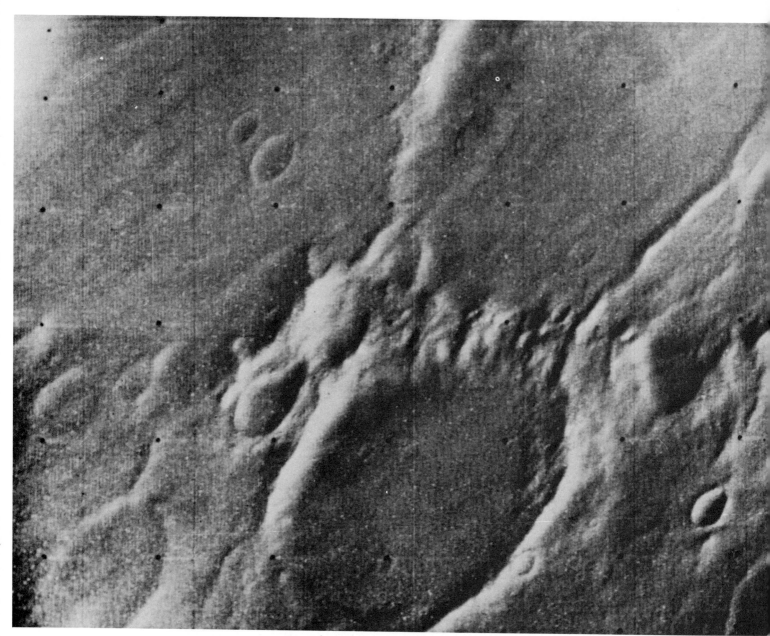

ABOVE: *"Giant's Footprint."* Two craters create the illusion of a large footprint on the south side of Mars in this Mariner 7 image. OPPOSITE: *Jupiter's Io.* The Jovian moon is visible directly above the planet's North Pole in this enhanced Pioneer 11 photograph.

ABOVE: *Phobos*. Mars' larger moon, Phobos, as viewed by Mariner 9. The image was computer enhanced for greater detail. OPPOSITE: *Deimos*. The smaller and outermost of Mars' two moons, Deimos, is revealed in this Viking image that has been deemed the best made up to this point. It is a tiny moon (the illuminated portion of this picture measures a mere 7½ by 5 miles) with many craters.

RIGHT: *Crater Mountains*. The semicircular mountains on the left of this Mariner 10 mosaic form the boundary of the Caloris Basin on Mercury. BELOW: *Mercury's South Pole*. More than two hundred Mariner 10 photos were combined to form this image of Mercury's Southern Hemisphere. OPPOSITE: *Venus*. Almost the full planet is visible in this composite of Mariner 10 television images. Cloud patterns which can be seen reveal the planet's upper atmosphere.

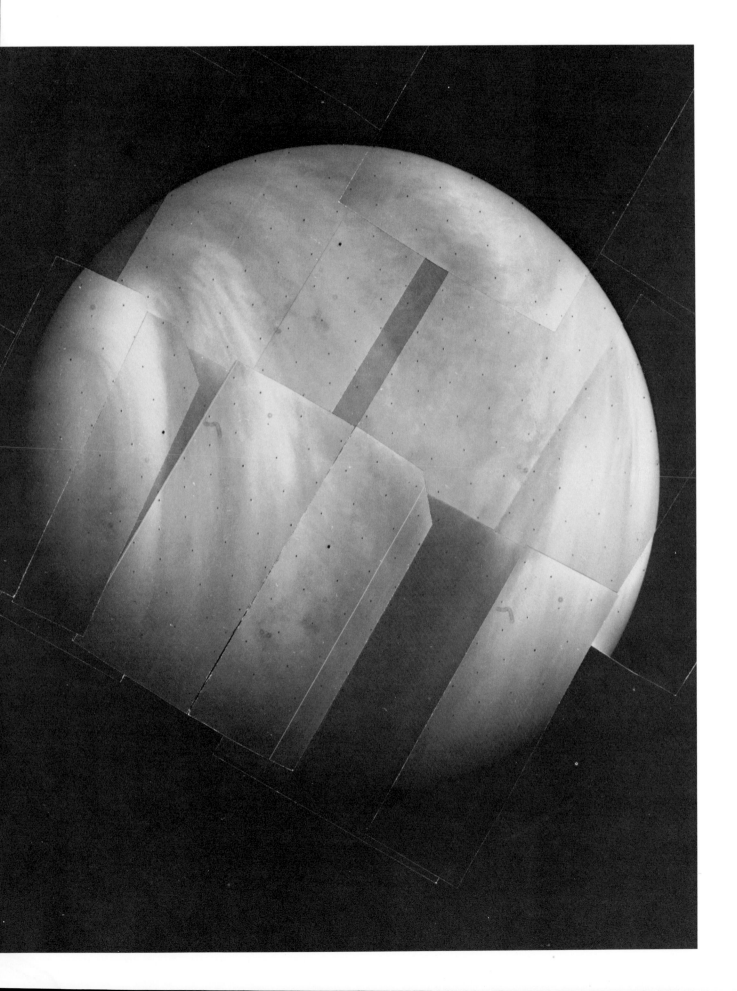

TOP: *Alligator in Black and White*. The shroud-befouled Gemini 9 target vehicle is, perhaps, even more sinister looking in black and white than in color. BOTTOM: *Bold Cameraman*. Russell L. Schweickart operating his Hasselblad during a period of Apollo 9 extravehicular activity.

Moon from 2,000 Miles. Lunar Orbiter 4 picture of the moon featuring the north polar region.

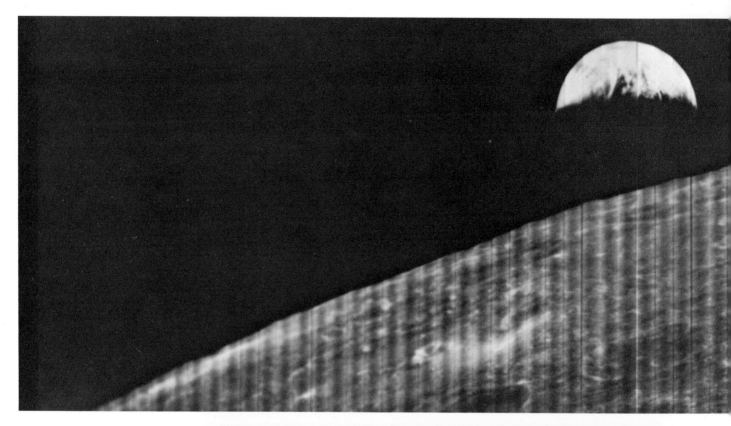

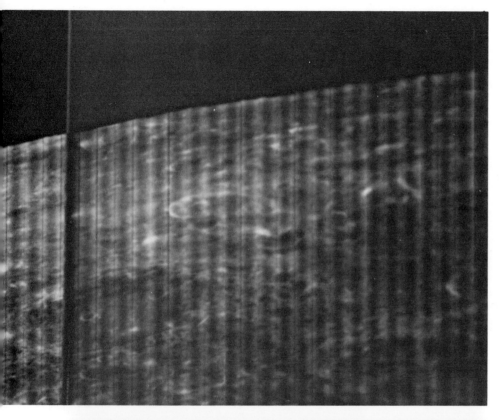

The First Glimpse of the Earth from the Moon. This over-the-shoulder view of the earth was made by Lunar Orbiter 1 on August 23, 1966 from a point 730 miles above the far side of the moon. At this angle, the east coast of the United States is at the top of the earth where it is afternoon.

FAR LEFT: *Crescent Earthrise.* A final view of the earth from the moon was taken from Apollo 17, the last manned lunar flight, against the battered surface of the far side of the moon. LEFT: *Manned Intervention.* The manned lunar module, the lunar surface, and the earth all appear in this photograph taken from the Apollo 11 command module.

Hortensius. The crater near the center of this Lunar Orbiter 3 picture is Hortensius—one of the smallest named craters. It is about 20 miles wide.

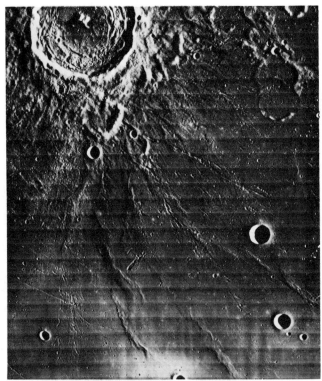

Taruntius. The large crater in this Lunar Orbiter 1 photograph is noteworthy because of its relative shallowness. Pictures like this have given geologists enough new information concerning the moon to keep them busy for years to come.

Far Side from Apollo 11. This photograph taken from lunar orbit has a strong three-dimensional quality to it.

Far Side from Apollo 10. The features in this oblique view from lunar orbit show a smoother and less dramatic topography.

Soil Collector. Apollo 12 astronaut carries lunar soil collected during the mission. The list on his left sleeve tells him the assignments he must complete while on the surface.

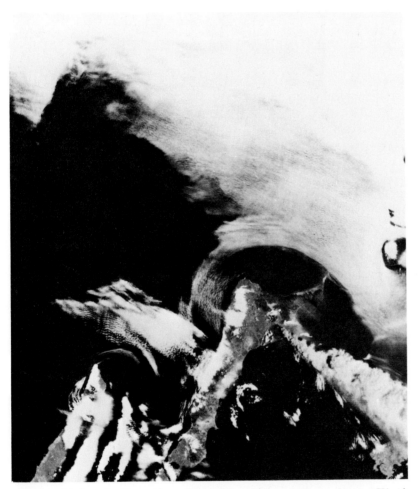

ABOVE: *Volcanic Eruption.* Landsat captures the volcano Tiatia on the Siberian island of Kunashir in its first eruption since 1812. The plume of ash-laden gases visible in the picture rose to heights of 15,000 feet during the eruption. OPPOSITE: *Dead Sea.* Salt evaporators on the Dead Sea can be seen in this Gemini 5 photograph taken over Jordon.

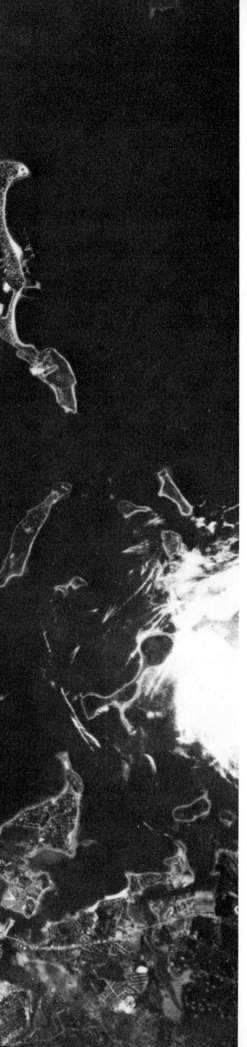

Boston. Metropolitan area viewed from
a high-altitude NASA Earth Resources
aircraft.

Chicago. In this Skylab 3 photograph, Chicago, Hammond, Gary, Aurora, Joliet, and East Chicago are all clearly visible.

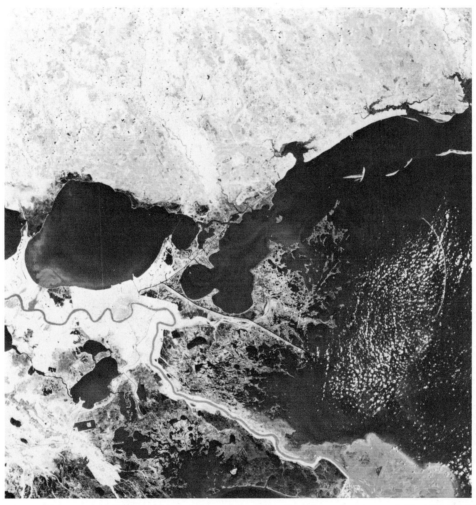

New Orleans at Flood Time. This and other Landsat images of the flooded areas of Louisiana taken in April, 1975 were used by the state to assess damage and to plan relief efforts.

Bay Area. San Francisco and Oakland as seen by the crew of Skylab 4. Like so many other urban photographs taken from space, it is remarkably detailed.

Los Angeles. In this Landsat image the Los Angeles metropolitan area sprawls along the coast at the bottom of the picture. The tiny squares at the upper left are cultivated fields.

New England. Cape Cod, Massachusetts, Connecticut, Rhode Island, and New York all appear in this Skylab 2 earth image.

BELOW LEFT: *Canton Area.* Canton is in the center of this Landsat photograph, and the Hsi Chiang River runs from left middle to center bottom. BELOW RIGHT: *Stalingrad.* The city of Stalingrad and the Volga River dominate this Landsat image taken over the USSR.

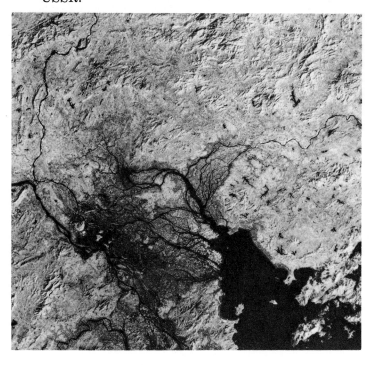 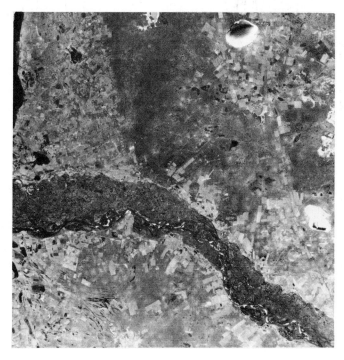

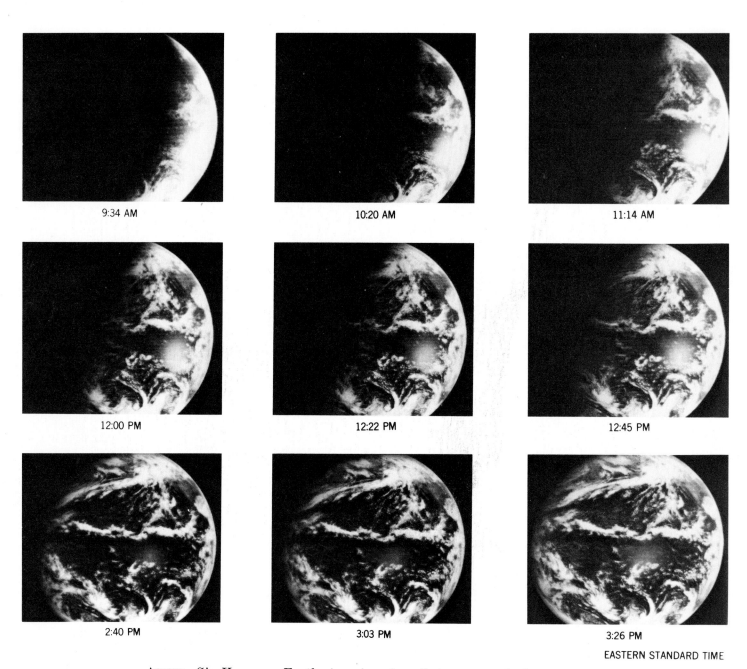

9:34 AM

10:20 AM

11:14 AM

12:00 PM

12:22 PM

12:45 PM

2:40 PM

3:03 PM

3:26 PM

EASTERN STANDARD TIME

ABOVE: *Six Hours on Earth*. A series of earth images made by the Applications Technology Satellite 1 on January 28, 1967. Later satellites beginning with ATS 3 were able to make images of the whole earth. OPPOSITE: *Full Disc*. The first image to be sent back by the GOES-1 Synchronous Meteorological Satellite in 1975. The outline of South America is very clear.

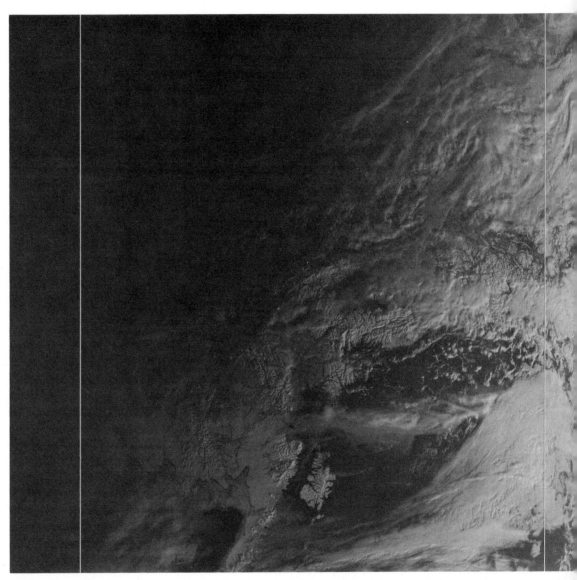

ABOVE: *Alaskan Volcano*. In this January, 1976 NOAA 4 picture of Alaska of a volcano on Augustine Island near the mouth of Cook Inlet, the plume of ash and smoke rises from the lower center of the picture and drifts toward the right edge. The island below and slightly to the right of the volcano is Kodiak Island. OPPOSITE: *The Mediterranean*. View from NOAA 4 taken in May, 1976.

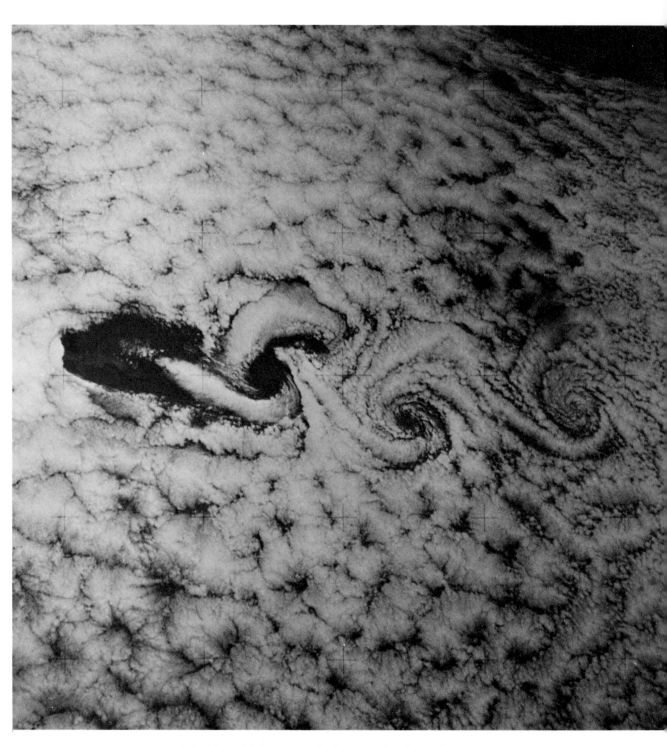

Vortices. This unusual view of cloud vortices was taken from Sky-lab 3 off the coast of Baja California and Mexico.

Hurricane Gladys. This intensely powerful hurricane never hit land, but that was not known when this picture was taken on October 1, 1975. Florida and Cuba look like easy targets.

Stormy August. Four large storms are at play over the Northern Hemisphere in the Synchronous Meteorological Satellite picture taken on August 31, 1975. The storms, of course, are the large swirling masses.

Hurricane Pack. In this truly remarkable image from GOES 2, three hurricanes appear in a line across the Pacific. The picture was taken on September 26, 1976. The west coast of the United States and Mexico are visible at the upper right.

Hurricane Belle Moves Up the East Coast. In these five satellite images each taken a day apart from August 6 to August 10, 1976, the course of Hurricane Belle is documented dramatically. In the next to last image, it is slamming into the Middle Atlantic Coast, and in the final image it is dissipating. Belle inflicted most of its damage on coastal New Jersey and Long Island.

Belle and Hyacinth. In this synoptic view from GOES 1 on August 8, Belle can be seen on the East Coast, and Hyacinth is over the Pacific near Mexico.

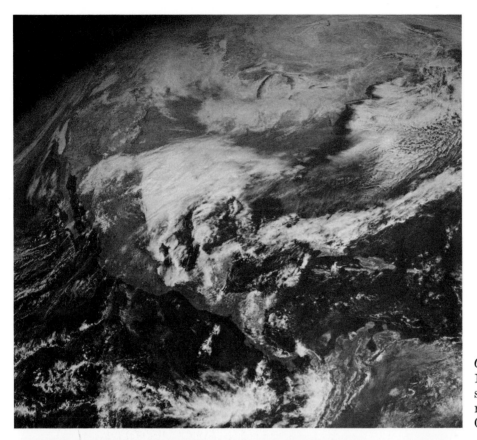

Cold Day in January. GOES 1 image of January 30, 1977 showing snow cover over the northern United States and Canada.

Great Lakes Winter. A portion of the bitter winter of 1977 as seen from the NOAA 5 satellite.

155

Nantucket Spill. NASA aircraft photograph of the oil spill that threatened the coast of Nantucket. Currently, spills are primarily monitored by aircraft; however, in the future the job will fall increasingly to earth-orbiting satellites.

Appendix

The Astronauts' Cameras and Film Types: from the Mercury Program through the First Lunar Landing.

Mission	Date	Astronaut(s)	Camera(s)	Film(s)
Mercury 6	2/20/62	Glenn	Ansco Auto-set 35	Color nega-tive (CN)
Mercury 7	5/24/62	Carpenter	Robot Re-corder 35	CN
Mercury 8	10/3/62	Schirra	Hasselblad 500C	Color Rever-sal (CR)
Mercury 9	5/16/63	Cooper	Hasselblad 500C	Assorted magazines (A)
Gemini 3	3/24/65	Grissom Young	Hasselblad 500C	CR
			McDonnell 16 mm	CR
Gemini 4	6/3/65	McDivitt White	Hasselblad 500C	CR
			Neiss-Con-tarex	CR Color in-frared (CI)
Gemini 5	8/21/65	Cooper Conrad	Hasselblad 500C	CR
			Neiss-Con-tarex	CR/CI
Gemini 6(A)	12/14/65	Schirra Stafford	Hasselblad 500C	A
Gemini 7	12/4/65	Borman Lovell	Hasselblad 500C	A
Gemini 8	3/16/66	Armstrong Scott	Hasselblad 500C	CR
Gemini 9	6/3/66	Stafford Cernan	Hasselblad 500C	CR
			Hasselblad Superwide	CR

Gemini 10	7/18/66	Young Collins	Hasselblad Superwide	CR
Gemini 11	9/12/66	Conrad Gordon	Hasselblad Superwide	CR
Gemini 12	11/11/66	Lovell Aldrin	Hasselblad Superwide	CR
Apollo 7	10/11/68	Schirra Eisele Cunningham	Hasselblad 500C	CR
Apollo 8	12/21/68	Borman Lovell Anders	Hasselblad 500C	CR
Apollo 9	3/3/69	McDivitt Scott Schweikart	Hasselblad 500C and Superwide	CR, both
Apollo 10	5/18/69	Cernan Young Stafford	Hasselblad 500C	CR
Apollo 11	7/16/69	Armstrong Aldrin Collins	Hasselblad 500C	CR
			Hasselblad Lunar Data Camera	CR
			Closeup Stereo ALSSC	CR

Hasselblad buffs may be interested in the camera's space record, which was tabulated at the time of the company's twenty-fifth anniversary in 1974. Keep in mind that the numbers have gone up and will continue to go up as Hasselblads fly on the Space Shuttle. There had been 23 flights involving 31 astronauts who had used 52 Hasselblads of which there were four different models. Some 33,000 pictures had been taken with them in space from 266 magazines. The cameras had made 956 orbits of the earth and 386 lunar orbits—adding up to more than 40 million miles of space travel with Hasselblads. Ten of them were left on the moon, and one was lost in space and now orbits the earth.